MW00633771

The Complete Anti-Inflammatory Diet Cookbook for Beginners

Comprehensive Guide with Quick & Easy Recipes to Heal Your Immune System, Prevent Chronic Diseases and Restore Your Body

2-Week Meal Plan Included

By

Anna Lor

Table of Content

Introduction

Inflammation helps the body battle disease and defends it against damage. It is an essential part of the healing process in most cases.

However, certain people have a medical disorder that does not function as well as the immune system should. This failure can lead to persistent or recurrent low inflammation.

Chronic inflammation occurs in multiple conditions. The anti-inflammatory diet is not a particular diet but a way to eat. An example of anti-inflammatory diets is the Mediterranean diet and the DASH diet.

There are ingredients in some foods that can cause or intensify inflammation. This is true for sugar or refined foods, while whole foods are less likely to have this effect, while new.

A new fruit and vegetable anti-inflammatory diet. Many herbal foods are healthy antioxidant sources. However, some foods can cause free radicals. Examples include foods which people fry in heated cooking oil over and over.

Nutritional antioxidants are food molecules that help eradicate free radicals from the body. Free radicals are the normal byproducts, like metabolism, of specific body processes. External factors like stress and smoking, however, may increase the number of free radicals in the body.

Free radicals cause damage to the cell. This harm raises the risk of inflammation and can lead to a number of diseases.

The body produces such antioxidants to assist in eliminating these toxic compounds, but also dietary antioxidants.

Chapter 1: The Anti-Inflammatory Diet

Inflammation is a standard mechanism to trigger healing by growing circulation for a biological intent. The immune and vascular system and the interplay of different chemical mediators is a complex mechanism. Increased circulation brings white blood cells and feeds to a site of injury or infection to kill and remedy the damage caused by invading pathogens. Inflammation is characterized by discomfort, swelling (tumor), heat and redness.

If the inflammation goes astray:

Although some inflammation is beneficial and suitable for cure, chronic or persistent inflammation, there is no damage to it. Chronic inflammation has a poor reputation as it has been involved in different disease processes like (but not limited to).

- Self-immune diseases
- Diabetes
- Arthritic disease
- Condition of Alzheimer
- Atherosclerosis (hardening of the artery leading to heart and stroke)
- ADD & ADHD
- Bowel disease inflammatory
- Asthma and allergies
- Disease

Soft tissue swelling and inflammatory chemical mediators can irritate nerve endings and lead to pain.

What is anti-inflammatory nutrition?

It is common knowledge that various foods are metabolized differently, with some encouraging and reducing inflammation. The goal of the anti-inflammatory diet is to promote optimal health and cure by selecting foods which reduce inflammation. If excessive inflammation is managed effectively by natural means (like diet), it decreases the dependency on anti-inflammatory drugs, which have undesirable and harmful side effects and do not fix the underlying issue. Though anti-inflammatory medication (like NSAIDs) is a fast way to relieve symptoms, it eventually weakens the immune system by destroying the gastrointestinal tract, which plays a significant role in the function of the immune system.

Anti-inflammatory diet fundamentals:

Typically, eat plenty of fresh fruit and vegetables, whole grains, anti-inflammable fats and minerals while avoiding food processed, refined sugar, milk products, animal protein, flavors and food sensitivities.

Plants:

Enjoy and eat:

Enjoy a wealth of new vegetables and fruits in a number of colors. Fruits and vegetables are filled with minerals, antioxidants and vitamins that provide the body with critical health building blocks. Examples are beans, lint, squash, candy, avocado, cruciferous fruits, dark leafy greens. There are so many options! The fruit is especially useful as pineapple and papaya are high in bromelain, which is a potent natural anti-inflammatory. Other excellent, balanced snacks include fruits and vegetables.

Avoid / Limit:

Avoid goods that are not organically grown. Herbicides and pesticides' toxic chemical residues may remain, and foreign irritants may be absorbed into the environment. Many crops in North America are already genetically modified and sold in order to assess protection for human consumption, without any objective scientific research. Independent research is eventually conducted to explain the harmful effects of genetically engineered species. International DNA is incorporated randomly into the crop genome. Examples include herbicide-resistant maize and soy made by Monsanto that are resistant to Roundup. In North America, nearly 90% of all maize and soy sold are genetically modified. Be conscious of genetically modified ingredients derivatives (e.g. maize starch, maize syrup, etc.). GMOs have also been proposed as a factor in the spike in allergies since our bodies perceive these foods as aliens. You will prevent both GMOs and harmful pesticides/herbicides by selecting products on the "certified organic" mark.

For certain people, nightshade vegetables may be a problem. Tomatoes, eggplant, and potatoes are examples of night-shades. Nightshades contain alkaloids that are expected to worsen inflammation and joint damage in specific individuals who are prone to arthritis (although evidence is contradictory). Thus, reducing or avoiding nightshade vegetables may be helpful for certain people.

Fats:

Enjoy feating:

Discover safe anti-inflammatory fats, including coconut oil, olive oil, avocados, sardines, and salmon. In humans, linoleic acid (omega-6) and alpha-linolenic acid (Omega-3) are two essential fatty acids. These are "important" since the body does not synthesize them because they are necessary for good health. Omega-3 are anti-inflammatory fats. Omega-6 fats can be anti-inflammatory or pro-inflammatory (as two separate pathways may be metabolized). Researchers say that it is easier to preserve the omega-6 to the omega-3 ratio from 2:1 to 4:1. The modern diet is also high in omega-6, as it is commonly available in cooking oils. It is therefore essential to include rich sources of omega-3 (such as flax, walnuts and fish in particular).

Avoid / Limit:

Fats like margarine, butter, hydrogenated oils, trans-fats, milk fat and saturated fats that are reduced or avoided. In safflower oil, sunflower oil, and maize oil, omega-6 fats are very high. Trans-fats are associated with inflammatory conditions.

Meat:

Eat and enjoy:

Limit animal proteins usually because they appear to acidify the body and therefore cause inflammation. Enjoy fish, poultry (mostly free-range, organically raised), lamb and omega-3 eggs when selecting animal protein.

Avoid / Limit:

Beef, pork, shellfish and farmed eggs are limited. Grass-fed is usually equivalent to grain-fed. Stop foods such as cold cuts. Cold cuts contain cancer-enhancing nitrates and nitrites. Barbecue food includes polycyclic aromatic hydrocarbons (PAHs) and heterocyclic amines (HCAs).

Dairy:

Enjoy and eat:

Enjoy mild milk alternatives (e.g., almond milk).

Avoid / Limit:

Avoid or limit total dairy products. Yogurt, milk, cheese and ice cream are included. When we age, we lose the enzyme that digests milk, which contributes to lactose intolerance and inflammation.

Grains:

Enjoy and eat:

Discover whole grains in comparison to processed grains. Refined grains are grains that extract the germ and bran. This means that fiber, minerals and vitamins are lost. In other terms, in exchange for longer shelf life, the good things are eliminated. Examples of healthy grains include whole oats/wheat, bulgar /couscous (organic), quinoa and oats (e.g. steel cuts) as well as entire grains.

Whole grains also constitute a rich source of complex carbohydrates. Complex carbohydrates (in comparison to simple sugars) eliminate blood sugar spikes. Sugar encourages swelling.

Avoid / Limit:

Stop or limit processed carbohydrates such as white bread, baked goods, candy and pasta.

Nuts:

Enjoy eating and enjoying:

Discover nuts and kinds of butter including almonds, sesame seeds, walnuts, flax and pumpkin seeds.

Avoid / Limit:

Stop specific allergies to nutrients.

Drinks:

Enjoy and eat:

Take advantage of plenty of clean, filtered water (preventing chlorine, fluoride and other inflammatory irritants). Lemon water and herbal teas are other great options.

Avoid / Limit:

Stop succulent sodas, fruit juice (with added sugar) and milk.

Spices:

Eat and enjoy:

Many spices minimize swelling. Examples include oregano, turmeric, ginger, rosemary, cinnamon and garlic. Bioflavonoids and polyphenols suppress inflammation and battle radicals free from disease. Cayenne pepper also contains capsicum and is anti-inflammatory. Capsicum is also used in creams for pain relief.

Sweeteners:

Eat and enjoy:

Enjoy stevia, maple syrup, molasses and honey in refined sugar as healthier alternatives.

Avoid / Limit:

Ignore refined sugar, fructose and, in particular, high fructose maize syrup that facilitates inflammation. Stop man-made sweeteners.

Other:

Enjoy and eat:

Enjoy fermented foods such as sauerkraut, kimchi and miso soup. Fermented foods are probiotics and help repair the immune system by promoting healthy intestinal microflora and reducing inflammation. Fermented foods are also easy to absorb and vitamin B factories.

Avoid / Limit:

Eliminate processed foods, artificial colors, artificial tastes and preservatives in general. Stop even foods with a known reaction or allergy to which inflammation promotes. Sensitivities in low grades are likely to miss, so take a food allergy test if you are unsure. Some of the most popular foodstuffs that cause problems include wheat (gluten), maize, soy and milk.

Everything we need for health can be contained in nature. We just have to make the right decision. There are a lot of anti-inflammatory nutritional recipes available if you need guidance and suggestions about what to eat.

Who Should Eat the Anti-Inflammatory Diet?

Were you aware of inflammation as the basis of most chronic diseases - diseases such as arthritis, obesity, heart disease, diabetes, and even cancer? That's right. The majority of chronic diseases derive from a lifestyle of privilege that encourages us to consume the wrong food in the incorrect quantity at the wrong time. These food choices take place in your body in a variety of processes that cause inflammation from a number of sources. Furthermore, many of us are genetically conditioned to excessive inflammation when exposed to common irritants like smoke, chemicals and dietary problems. Some of us trigger so much inflammation that we have auto-immune diseases like MS, lupus, rheumatoid arthritis, colitis and psoriasis.

How exactly are terrible food choices causing inflammation? Some of the worst culprits are frozen and highly processed foods and fast foods. They are perhaps some of the most commonly available food options. These foods are designed for convenience and filled with trans-fat to improve their shelf-life and change their taste and texture, and the trans-fat consists of a saturated natural fat-another less than healthy fat. The saturated fat is "transformed" into fat by a trans-hydrogenation process. This transformed fat is chemically very different from a natural fat that creates a cascade of chemicals called cytokines when incorporated into your body tissues. Cytokines are molecules that cause inflammation in your body.

Even inflammatory foods filled with refined sugars. Cakes, doughnuts and cookies are examples of easily digested foods that release significant quantities of glucose. Your body consumes glucose quickly, triggering high blood glucose. Your body releases an insulin rush to help normalize your blood glucose levels. This insulin rush along with high blood glucose contributes to cytokines, inflammatory molecules and the release of your body. In reality, every glucose surge signals that your body stores fat. Guess what? Fat tissue is physiologically active and starts releasing the same inflammatory molecules and cytokines.

Refined grains – fiber extracted grains and essential nutrients – often cause inflammation. An entire grain is a molecule of large quantities of glucose bound and encapsulated with a fiber sheet. This fiber coating slows down the absorption and release of glucose. If the outer fiber coating is removed to create a smooth and creamy texture, the glucose molecules can be easily digested and absorbed into your body. This rapid increase in glucose is the cause of the inflammatory cascade.

Some grains are capable of inducing inflammation in some people. Oats, Wheat, rye and barley are all grains that contain large quantities of a protein known as gluten. Gluten produces food, like bread, crooked outside and soft inside. However, this same gluten is particularly toxic in people with hereditary problems in the absorption of gluten. Symptoms such as discomfort, flushing, diarrhea, and malnutrition or mild nausea or energy deficiency can be severe. Remove these particular grains from your diet is also the secret to managing this form of inflammation.

What is an anti-inflammatory diet, exactly? An anti-inflammatory diet typically consists of fresh whole foods that do not contain inflammatory factors and are filled with molecules which actually neutralize inflammation in the body.

Phytonutrients, responsible for their colorful appearance, are present in most fruits and vegetables. These enormous molecules have both antioxidant and anti-inflammatory properties. This ensures that the oxidative stress your body creates every day, leading to inflammation, is neutralized. Healthy fats contained in fatty fish, cold water, flax seeds and nuts can also decrease your body's inflammation. Cooking oils like the olive oil or canola oil also help the body battle inflammation and neutralize it. In new, whole foods, some vitamins and minerals – vitamins A, zinc, vitamins D, vitamins E, selenium, vitamins C, and copper – are present in abundance. They also neutralize oxidative stress and dampen inflammation development.

The first step in the anti-inflammatory diet is to avoid fast foods and processed food. The second stage is the reduction of foods with refined sugars and processed grains. The basis of the anti-inflammatory diet is a generous intake of fresh fruit or vegetables daily and a modest amount of whole grains, lean protein, as well as good fats found in fish, seeds and nuts. Then, the final step is to reduce or remove grain for selected persons, particularly gluten-containing grains.

And who's going to eat an inflammatory diet? Anyone suffering from inflammatory disorders like autoimmune disorders (lupus, multi-sclerosis, rheumatoid arthritis, colitis) or allergic disorders (gastrointestinal, eczema) certainly would benefit from the anti-inflammatory diet. Most people with chronic pain (headaches, neck pain, back pain, knee pain, muscle pain, joint pain), are inflammatory and benefit from their distress. Bowel syndrome irritable and popular digestive problems such as acid reflux improve with an anti-inflammatory diet. Fortunately, anyone with chronic degenerative conditions (diabetes, arthritis, obesity, cardiovascular diseases, and even cancer) can also benefit from that diet. Finally, someone involved in prevention and optimum wellbeing will benefit from degenerative diseases. The science indicates that ingestion, in order to avoid inflammation, not only prevents illness and protects health but also keeps us younger.

So eat healthily and do not allow the inflammation to grab you. All will benefit from this powerful way of eating from children to the elderly.

The Need Anti-Inflammatory Diet?

Inflammation is often triggered by an injury, you stub your toe and swell your toe. This is the fundamental inflammatory response. Some people also know that roughness around a wound is just a kind of inflammation the immune system uses to repair the injury. The fact that inflammation often exists inside the body is not widely understood. If the body is inflammatory, the risk of disease, cancer and heart disease can increase. This diet is an easy way to tackle these consequences and reduce today's harm.

From inflammation, I don't suffer!

This is the most famous and least accurate argument. Anyone in the world at any stage in their life is affected by inflammation. In western communities, such as the United States, a substantial part of the population is inflamed every day. The typical inflammatory disorder is obesity or overweight. This inflammatory reaction can be the cause of some weight-related conditions such as diabetes.

When fat cells expand, they occupy the free space of the liver. Blood flow can be decreased, and the body sometimes feels like it has to struggle to operate normally. Inflammation occurs as a natural, healing reaction when the organism feels threatened. Sadly, as opposed to the little cut that will be healed in a few short days. The longer the body lives, the greater the chance of long-term consequences, obesity takes time to correct.

If obesity is encountered, modifying the diet by decreasing calories decreases body weight and reduces body inflammation. This is the essential advantage of an anti-inflammatory diet. People who are overweight or obese are not the only ones who can benefit from an anti-inflammatory diet.

Treatment and prevention of disease

There are many infections and inflammatory disorders. Asthma, endometriosis, pelvic inflammatory diseases, arthritis, diabetes, psoriasis, COPD, colitis, inflammatory bowel syndrome, and lupus are only a few examples. Overall, there are actually almost 40 autoimmune diseases that are affected by inflammation in the medical community.

What do I do?

The first thing is to change the diet to reduce the inflammation of foodstuffs. Processed foods, pre-packaged foods and fast foods can contribute to increased inflammation of body. A substitution of this food with magic meats, healthy fats and whole grains would make a big difference in the response of the body to inflammation. In addition, if weight is an issue,

13

weight loss by shifting into an anti-inflammatory diet will exponentially increase the benefits.

An anti-inflammatory diet should not be modified in response to the illness or disease. Prevention is a good alternative, and anti-inflammatory diets can reduce the risk of many of the diseases mentioned. If the body feels like it has to fight for life, inflammation happens, so providing healthy, inflammatory foods is a great alternative, even for those who are young, active and don't feel like they need an anti-inflammatory diet.

Alkaline Anti-Inflammatory Diet

Our diet offers one of the best ways to stay healthy, alleviate chronic pain, maintain a desirable weight and encourage longevity. Sadly, many of us got the wrong details on what, how and when to eat.

A little human history is in order to begin. We were nomadic for much of the history of humans on this planet. We went around the world searching for big animals that could be killed and eaten. Otherwise, people stocked mammals such as sheep, goats and other cattle which needed to move to ample pastures. Our forefathers didn't eat much fat and meat. They gathered fruits and very little grain. There were very few starchy carbohydrates in their diet, including pasta, cereals, bread, and other grains. Just around 5000 years ago when Egyptians started farming did people begin to eat a lot of starchy carbohydrates.

Let's now add some fundamental biochemistry that is easy to understand. We have all learned of fish oil and its critical omega-3 fatty acids, also known as omega-3 oils. These omega-3 oils are useful to us, most understand. Another oil is omega-6 fatty acid, often ignored. The carbohydrates of our antecedents were ate few starchy and nomadic, and diet consisted around 1:1 of omega-3 and omega-six fatty acids. This ratio for body is excellent. It makes the body alkaline compared to acidic. The more alkaline we are, the better we are.

However, we become more acidic and more inflamed in the body if we get imbalanced in our omega-3 and omega-6 fatty acids. Further infection contributes to chronic pain, the gain of weight, and lifestyle-related diseases such as diabetes, cardiovascular disorders, arthritis, and other processes impacting us today. If we eat high levels of carbohydrates like wheat, maize and rice, we eat food with more omega-6 fatty acids. It can create a 1:10 omega-3 deficit to omega-6 fatty acids or more. For example, potato chips have a 1:60 ratio of omega-3 to omega-6 fatty acids.

Inflammation causes systemic, general inflammation in the body by the improper balance of the omega oils caused by too much carbohydrates. Conversely, a lower diet in carbohydrates encourages a ratio of 1:1 fatty acid that makes the body more productive.

An alkaline anti-inflammatory diet can be accomplished by eating less starchy carbs. If one consumes 100-200 grams of grain products per day, this will lead to a healthier lifestyle. This diet will definitely include significant quantities of vegetables and a fair range of foodstuffs containing protein and fats such as meats, eggs, nuts, and fish. This diet should be low in candy and sugar such as cookies, sweets, soda, sports drinks and cakes.

This diet must not be overly strict. Many people without severe metabolism can definitely have a "cheat day" or two a week where they might reach 100-200 grams of starchy carbohydrate and some sweets.

Not all health professionals or nutritionists will necessarily adhere to the specifics here. However, several books and medical practitioners are associated with this strategy. The Paleolithic Diet, South Beach Diet, the Keto Diet and the Mediterranean diet are some of these.

An expert will definitely find people who want this dietary strategy, who can provide them with more advice.

Many people who use an alkaline anti-inflammatory diet find that their health has improved in a reasonable period of time. Many of us who used this strategy initially noticed that we had a desirable weight within one year, removing back pain, improved energy and better sleep. While there may be no mainstream alkaline anti-inflammatory diet, there is definitely ample empirical and anecdotal evidence to examine this lifestyle.

Lose Weight and Be Great With Anti-Inflammatory Diet

You will feel fantastic from the anti-inflammatory diet by decreasing the intake of pro-inflammatory food thus decreasing discomfort and pressure of the joints and organs when these foods are stripped from the diet.

Your risk of weight loss also decreases when you adopt this diet. Other additional causes of inflammation in my body lead to: hypertension, arthritis, fibromyalgia, Alzheimer's disease, Chronic fatigue syndrome, chronic pain, asthma, cancer, acne, diabetes, cardiac disease, depression. This is, however, a condensed list where there are several other inflammatory conditions.

The less inflammatory food we eat, the less inflammation in our body.

Pro-inflammatory food background information:

Modern man's crops, hydrogen oils, refined sugars, seed oils and vegetable. These foods were around a short time, but obesity and disease are increasing. Human beings are genetically adapted for the ingestion of fruits, nuts, veggies, fish and meat, not chronic diseases related foods.

Why do grains burn?

Grains produce a protein known as gluten. Gluten is the primary cause of many stomach disorders, including coeliac disease and frequent headaches. They have sugar protein know as lectins, which has been shown to induce digestive inflammation. Grains also produce phytic acid that is believed to reduce calcium, iron, magnesium, and zinc absorption in the body.

Finally, grains contain high levels of biochemical fatty acids called omega-6 fatty acids, causing inflammation. Fatty acid biochemical are anti-inflammatory and present in fresh fish, and green vegetables are known as omega-3 fatty acids.

What do I have to eat?

Foods against inflammation

- All fruits (raw or lightly cooked)
- Red and delicious pumpkin
- Omega-3 anti-inflammatory eggs
- Raw noodles
- Turmeric, Ginger, garlic spices-
- Biological cocoa oil, butter, extra virgin olive oil.
- Fresh fish, prevent farming
- Chicken, Beef, grass-fed eggs

- Wild game like elk, deer, etc.
- Water, red wine, organic green tea, beer stout.

The Benefits of an Anti-Inflammatory Diet

Inflammation soon becomes the next significant medical breakthrough. People with obesity have inflammatory problems. Body inflammation is associated with diabetes, arthritis and asthma. Not to mention the link to such cardiac disorders and cancers. Reducing the body's inflammatory system with an anti-inflammatory diet will instantly improve the feeling, not to mention the long-term health and well-being benefits of dietary change.

The first step to an anti-inflammatory diet is to consider effects of food on the body. Meat supplies nutrients and body vitamins to survive. The idea of eating and not live to eat is a significant impetus for the weight loss group, but this idea should not only be pursued when a few pounds have to be lost. Some foods have high antioxidant concentrations and natural anti-inflammatory nutrients that can minimize the body's inflammatory impact. These are the cornerstones of the anti-inflammatory diet.

Omega 3 and other fatty acids Role

Many foods containing oil contain fatty acids. Fish like sardines and salmon are the best natural source. However, Omega 6 fatty acids are dominant over Omega 3s in Western diets. Since widely consumed foods like chicken, turkey, eggs, nuts and vegetable oils are rich in fatty acids from Omega 6. However, people don't know that these fatty acids must be balanced with Omega 3s to achieve optimum health and anti-inflammatory results. The bulk of Western diets contain Omega 6s 10 times more than Omega 3s. Some diets are up to 30 times higher. The ideal ratio is four Omega 6 components to each Omega 3 component.

Growing Omega 3 fatty acids in diet will reduce body inflammation and thus reduce the health and overall well being impact of this disorder. Omega-3s foods include fish oils, kiwis, black raspberries and assorted nuts. Flaxseeds are the most readily available source for Omega 3s. Many people make a mistake of fish oils for the best source, but flaxseed oils tend to have Omega

3s that make it easier to absorb. Flaxseed oils contain 55% ALA, an Omega 3 fatty acid, (alpha-linoleic acid).

Be Gone Fatty Meats

The reduction of fatty meats is another quick adjustment to minimize inflammation in the body. Red meat is so worst of all meats for inflammatory people. It is a safe idea to select a leaner cut or a slimmer substitute. Bison and venison are two types of containing less fat. Grass-fed cows have less harmful body properties as well. Meat, turkey, maize chicken, soya, soy and tofu milk are all magnificent options in order to minimize inflammation. In Omega 6s, however, some of these meats appear to be higher. To tackle fatty acid disequilibrium, consider cooking these meats in olive oil, or adding flaxseed oil to the final dish to improve Omega 3s. To increase inflammation.

The risk of food production

Refined carbohydrate is the hardest thing to consume while inflamed. Their nutritional value is very low and should be supplemented by full-grain alternatives. Every flour is wheat-based, but refined flour is whole and bleached with the safe grain. What remains are wasted calories that would undoubtedly further swell the body. This can make some difference on how your body responds to your diet simply substitutes white bread with whole-grain bread and white flour with unbleached whole wheat flour.

The Anti-Inflammatory Diet Natural Breakfast

One of the secrets of alleviating pain and chronic inflammation is to consider your kitchen's capacity. This is the food that you cook and consume to restore your body in your home.

We will create a perfect, natural anti-inflammatory breakfast that gives you energy and a great start to your day. Interested? Excellent.

Firstly, let me introduce you to the extraordinary culinary discovery of the last 100 years. The magic mixer. No, not the juicer that removes the essential fiber from everything. Nor does the food processor that makes just a decent knife and spoon and takes away the cooking meditation.

The Hamilton Shake starts with a natural anti-inflammatory breakfast many times per week.

Nothing comes from a silicone bath at an immense cost from a health clinic, which is really very economical. That's how it goes:

The Anti-Inflammatory Food Ingredients

Cut a pear into chunks and place it in the blender. It may also be an apple, grapefruit, mango, papaya or kiwi, depending on what is in the foodstuffs.

Add half a cup of my sunflower, sesame, flax and calf mixture. This offers essential fatty acids (omega-3) and protein with all the fibers of the whole crop. Mix them and store them in the refrigerator in a large container.

Then add berries, the dark berries, blueberries, blackberries and so on are full of antioxidants called flavonoids and as fair as the exotic, high-priced Amazonian stuff. They really freeze well.

That's the cornerstone. And there are the mega extras:

Adding turmeric is one of nature's most delicate anti-inflammatory plants. Fresh Burdock root, a wonderful herb that cleanses the liver and blood.

The nettle season is where I live, and I choose it from the wilderness.

When you mix them, they don't sting you. The combination inactivates the sting and natural minerals and the anti-inflammatory results are right for you and reduce allergies.

It is also possible to add cut raw carrots or celery.

Here's the key: put everything else according to your mood. Your imagination and your increasing level of knowledge are the only limits.

Play with it. You will save hundreds of dollars in vitamins and medicines.

Add water and blend until smooth, add cold or warm water (almond milk is also acceptable) to ensure your favorite consistency. Save any for later if you have more than you need for breakfast.

This mix is healthy food for nutrients and a tolerated delivery mechanism for vast amounts of nutrients and medicinal herbs. It can be used for breakfast or at any other time.

The Biggest Struggles of an Anti-Inflammatory Diet

Everyone needs to feel better and live healthier. One of the most straightforward approaches is to turn from a conventional west diet to an inflammatory diet. Make the change simple, but similar to a diet, and it can be challenging to adhere to the food changes and see what you consume.

Fast food and inflammation

Fast food is an enormous barrier to the anti-inflammatory diet. Foods rich in fat appear to increase inflammation in the body three to four hours after the meal. If the same amount of calories used in one fast-food were consumed as fresh vegetables, fruit, and lean meats, it would not cause this effect. Free radicals, cell killers that compound inflammation issues, can also be increased by 175% following fast food intake.

The alternative - A substitution, anti-inflammatory diet is the perfect alternative to fast food. Take McDonald's Big Mac into account. This sandwich is made of lean turkey and a whole grain bun. The "unique" sauce can be combined with lower carbohydrate ketchup, mayonnaise, olive oil and free from sugar. The result is a delicious substitute with a much lower fat count.

Red meat, milk and your flame

Science has failed for a long time to relate red meat to some types of cancer. They knew nothing about the research that would associate this popular dinner protein with inflammation. Researchers conclude that the body responds protectively to some chemical elements of red meat and milk. The immune system will kick in if the body thinks these are foreign substances and inflammation takes place. Imagine eating red meat once a day and drinking 2 to 3 cups of milk. The body will live in a state of persistent or chronic inflammation that over time could cause health problems.

Lean meat, beef and fish are all part of a balanced diet. Beef is an excellent source of iron, which does not inherently remove it. However, the option of leanest cuts is essential for good health. Lean proteins and beans are the safest meats.

Trans-fats and the flame

Trans-fatty acid is a secret cause of body inflammation. While many people know a little bit about this kind of fat, few understand the effects on the body. Fast food, baked goods, pre-packaged food and margarine are also strong trans-fat sources. These fats can increase the risk of coronary artery disease, insulin resistance, diabetes and cardiac failure following the entry into the body. There is also a greater chance of stroke because of abnormally high levels of lipid. While many foods claim to be free of trans-fat, that is not the whole reality. These foods can contain up to 0.5 g of trans-fats per serving and still mark the product as "trans-fat-free," as specified in the labelling guidelines. There are small quantities if the diet is high in processed foods, margarine and baked goods over time.

The Choice - Natural fats such as whole butter and olive oil have no trans-fats. It is a successful first step to select these instead of hydrogenated oils and margarine. There is no alternative but to remove them from the diet all together when it comes to foods cooked in trans-fat. Many people prefer an anti-inflammatory diet by preparing "fast foods" at home with their own snacks.

Chapter 2: 2-Week Meal Plan with All Slow Cooked Recipes

Week One

DAY ONE

BREAKFAST

Slow-Cooker Southwest Quinoa Bowls

This taco-bowl-style recipe will reach adults and children alike. The sitting time of 10 minutes so let cheese melt in the quinoa, making the dish super decadent. If Cheddar-Jack is not found, use Sharp Cheddar or Monterey Jack. Garnish with lime wedges, fresh cilantro, and more cheese if wished.

Ingredients

• 1 yellow onion (about 8 ounces), chopped
• 1 tablespoon olive oil
• 1 ripe avocado, cubed
• 1 teaspoon ground cumin
• 1 red bell pepper (about 8 ounces), chopped
• 3 garlic cloves, minced (about one tablespoon)
• ¾ teaspoon kosher salt
• 1 (15 ounces) can no-salt-added black beans, drained and rinsed

• 1 teaspoon ancho chili powder
• 1 (14.5 ounces) can fire-roasted diced tomatoes
• frozen corn kernels (from 1 ear) or 1 cup fresh
• 2 cups water
• 1 cup uncooked quinoa, rinsed
• ¼ cup chopped fresh cilantro
• 4 ounces Cheddar-Jack cheese blend, shredded (about 1 cup)

Directions

• **Step 1:** Heat the oil over medium-high in the large saucepan. Add the onions and bell pepper, cook, always stirring, for four to five minutes, until tender. Add the garlic, cumin and powder of chili; cook and frequently stir for 1 minute. In a slow cooker, combine the onion mixture, maize, black beans, water, tomatoes, quinoa and salt. Cover and cook Medium, 4 to 5 hours until the quinoa is tender and the liquid is nearly absorbed.

• **Step 2:** Apply the cilantro to the slow cooker and blend well. Sprinkle the cheese with the quinoa mixture; cover and let stand about 10 minutes until the cheese is melted. Divide the mixture into six bowls; apply the avocado uniformly.

Nutrition Facts
Serving Size: About 1 Cup
364 calories; carbohydrates 44g 14% DV; protein 15g 30% DV; exchange other carbs 3; sugars 7g; dietary fiber 10g 40% DV fat 16g 25% DV; cholesterol -1mg; saturated fat 5g 25% DV; vitamin a iu -1IU; sodium 536mg 21% DV; folate -1mcg; vitamin c -1mg -2% DV; calcium -1mg; magnesium -1mg; iron -1mg -6% DV; potassium -1mg; thiamin -1mg -100% DV.

LUNCH
Italian Wedding Soup
This Italian wedding soup recipe is the best in Italian comfort, and this simple soup recipe offers countless variations. Replace the kale or escarole, chard, chicory or other leafy green and any leftover white bean cooked (or canned), in the healthy Italian wedding soup recipe.

Ingredients
• 1-pound ground turkey breast
• ¼ teaspoon salt
• ½ cup dry white wine
• 1 large egg, lightly beaten
• 1 cup fresh whole-wheat breadcrumbs
• ¼ cup finely chopped fresh parsley

• 1 tablespoon Worcestershire sauce
• 2 cloves garlic, minced
• ½ teaspoon crushed fennel seeds
• ½ teaspoon freshly ground pepper
• 2 teaspoons extra-virgin olive oil

Soup
• 1 tablespoon extra-virgin olive oil
• 1 cup chopped carrots (2 medium)

• 1 cup chopped onion (1 medium)
• 4 cups chopped cabbage (about 1/2 small head)

- 1 cup chopped celery (2 medium stalks)
- 1 (15 ounces) can one 15-ounce can white beans, rinsed
- 8 cups coarsely chopped escarole or thinly sliced kale leaves (about one bunch)
- 8 cups low-sodium chicken broth
- ½ cup freshly grated Romano cheese

Direction
• Step 1:
In a big bowl, combine turkey with breadcrumbs, Worcestershire, egg, garlic, Persil, the seed of fennel, pepper and salt. Refrigerate to firm for 10 minutes. Shape the mixture into 32 (1-inch) meatballs with damp hands (approx. 1 tablespoon each).

Step 2:
In a wide non-stick skillet heat 2 teaspoons of oil over medium heat. Attach the meatballs and cook until browned 7-9 minutes on all sides. Remove from heat and apply wine to remove brown bits gently. Remove from the heat.

Step 3
Preparing soup: heat one tablespoon oil over medium heat in a soup pot or Dutch oven. Add onion, carrots, celery, and cook, stirring for 7 to 9 minutes until the onion is translucent. Add cook and cod, stirring, for another 5 minutes. Stir in broth, rice, escarole, meatballs and some juices. Stir. Bring to a boil, reduce heat to cook and cook for 20 to 25 minutes and stir periodically until the vegetables are soft. Top with one tablespoon of grated cheese each section.

Nutrition Facts
Serving Size: About 1 3/4 Cups with 4 Meatballs
protein 23.9g 48% DV; 283.7 calories; carbohydrates 23.5g 8% DV; exchange other carbs 1.5; sugars 4.6g; dietary fiber 6.3g 25% DV fat 11.1g 17% DV; cholesterol 60.1mg 20% DV; saturated fat 3.5g 18% DV; vitamin c 21.9mg 37% DV; vitamin a iu 4130.1IU 83% DV folate 141.5mcg 35% DV; iron 3.3mg 18% DV; calcium 205.7mg 21% DV; magnesium 33.3mg 12% DV; sodium 522.5mg 21% DV; potassium 869.9mg 24% DV; thiamin 0.1mg 14% DV.

Exchanges: 1 1/2 Vegetable, 2 Medium-Fat Meat, 1/2 Starch, 1/2 Lean Meat, 1/2 Fat

DINNER
Chicken and Farro Herb Salad
This healthy chicken salad recipe makes an excellent potting plate or healthy dinner with lots of fresh herbs, arugula, olives and farro. We love the sweet taste and fast food of Farro, but even good choices are made for other grains, such as Freekeh, Bulgur or couscous.

Ingredients
Red-Wine Vinaigrette
- ⅓ cup red-wine vinegar
- ½ cup extra-virgin olive oil
- 1 ½ tablespoons Dijon mustard

Salad
- 3 cups water
- 1 ½ pounds boneless, skinless chicken breast, trimmed
- 1 cup farro
- ½ teaspoon kosher salt
- ¼ teaspoon ground pepper
- 1 cup diced carrot
- 1 fennel bulb, cored and chopped
- 1 cup chopped seeded English cucumber

- ¾ teaspoon kosher salt
- 1 small clove garlic, minced
- ½ teaspoon ground pepper

- ¼ cup chopped flat-leaf parsley
- ½ cup finely chopped red onion
- ¼ cup fresh basil, very thinly sliced
- 2 cups arugula, tough stems removed, coarsely chopped
- ¼ cup fresh mint, very thinly sliced
- ¼ cup oil-cured black olives, sliced

Directions
Step 1: Vinaigrette: vinegar of whisk, garlic, mustard, salt of 3/4 teaspoon and 1/2 tea cubicle in a medium cup. Oil whisk.

Step 2: Prepare salad: In a medium cup, bring the water to a boil. Add the farro, reduce heat to a minimum, cover and cook for 15 to 25 minutes, until tender. Drain; move the farro into a big tub.

Step 3: Toss 1/3 of a cup of vinaigrette with the soft farro.

Step 4: Grill to medium-high preheat.

Step 5: Sprinkle salt and the pepper with chicken. Grill rack petroleum (see tip). Grill the chicken, turning once or twice, 12 to 16 minutes until cooked. Let it cool and slice for 5 minutes.

Step 6: Stir into the farro fennel, cucumber, carrot, onion, basil, parsley, mint and one-third cup of vinaigrette.

Step 7: Stir arugula in the farro mixture just before serving. Serve with chicken and olives and the remaining vinaigrette. Serve well.

Nutrition Facts
Serving Size: 1 1/3 Cups Salad & 3 Oz. Chicken

Exchanges: 1 1/2 Vegetable, 1 1/2 Starch, 3 Lean Meat, 4 Fat 458.8 calories; carbohydrates 31.9g 10% DV; protein 28.2g 56% DV; exchange other carbs 2; sugars 4.8g; dietary fiber 5.3g 21% DV fat 24.5g 38% DV; saturated fat 3.7g 19% DV; vitamin a iu 4562.4IU 91% DV; cholesterol 62.7mg 21% DV; vitamin c 12.7mg 21% DV; calcium 86.4mg 9% DV; folate 38mcg 10% DV iron 2.7mg 15% DV; potassium 529.9mg 15% DV; magnesium 44.3mg 16% DV; sodium 512.6mg 21% DV; thiamin 0.1mg 9% DV.

DAY TWO
BREAKFAST

Italian Roasted Pork Tenderloin with Vegetables and Quinoa

For the good taste in this simple roasted pork tenderloin dish, marinate pork the night before or take it before going to work in the morning. Then, once you get home, all you have to do is roast pork and vegetables and make the quinoa for this safe and simple dinner. This recipe makes more quinoa and use the remains as a basis for fast lunch, salads, fried food later in a week.

Ingredients
Italian Dressing
•

- ¾ cup red-wine vinegar
- 1 ½ tablespoons sugar
- 5 tablespoons water

- 1 ¾ cups extra-virgin olive oil
- 1 large clove garlic
- 1 tablespoon Dijon mustard

- 2 teaspoons dried basil
- ½ teaspoon salt
- Pork; Vegetables
- 1-pound pork tenderloin
- 2 medium parsnips
- 3 tablespoons extra-virgin olive oil
- 4 medium carrots
- 1 crown of medium broccoli
- Quinoa
- ¼ teaspoon salt
- 3 cups low-sodium chicken broth
- 2 teaspoons dried oregano
- ½ teaspoon ground pepper
- 4 tablespoons balsamic glaze
- ¾ teaspoon ground pepper, divided
- 2 teaspoons Italian seasoning
- ¾ teaspoon salt, divided
- 1 ½ cups quinoa
- 1 tablespoon extra-virgin olive oil

Directions

Step1: Dressing: Mix the blender with the mixture of vinegar, basil, water, mustard, sugar, garlic, oregano, salt and pepper. Puree until smooth. Until smooth. Slowly apply oil and puree to the motor until creamy. (Measure 1/4 cup plus two tablespoons and pass the remaining dressing into a large stem jar; cool until one week.)

Step 2: For cooking pork and vegetables: place pork and 1/4 cup dressing in a wide sticky bag. Click air and lock. Massage the pork dressing in. Cold for a period of 4 hours or up to 24 hours. (Reserve the two tablespoons for Step 8 dressing.)

Step 3: In lower and upper thirds of an oven place racks; preheat to 425 F.

Step 4: Peel and cut parsnips and carrots into 1-inch bits. Cut broccoli into big blooms, approximately 1 1/2 inches across. Throw two cucumbers of oil, Italian seasoning and 1/2 teaspoon of salt and pepper into the vegetables. Spread on a broad baker's rimmed pan.

Step 5: Remove pork at the marinade and toss it dry with towels of paper. Sprinkle each salt and pepper with the remaining 1/4 teaspoon. Heat the one tablespoon remaining of oil over medium-high heat in a large ovenproof skillet. Add cook and pork until browned 3 to 5 minutes on the one hand. Swallow the pork and pass it to the top rack. Place the vegetables on the bottom shelf.

Step 6: Roast pork until 145 degrees F is instantly read in the thickest portion, approximately 20 minutes. Stir and brown the vegetables once or twice, tenderly, for 20 to 25 minutes.

Step 7: Meanwhile, prepare quinoa: In a wide casserole combine broth, oil and salt. Bring over high heat to a frying glass. Remove the quinoa and return to a frying pan. Reduce the heat then cook until all the liquid has absorbed the quinoa, and all the grains explode 15-20 minutes. Remove from sun, cover and allow 5 minutes to stand. (For another usage, reserve 3 cups.)

Step 8: Switch your pork to a clean cutting board and allow 5 minutes to rest. Toss the remaining two tablespoons of dressing in the vegetables. Slice the pork and serve with the balsamic glaze roasted vegetables and quinoa.

Nutrition

Serving Size: 3 Oz. Pork, 1/2 Cup Quinoa & 1 Cup Vegetables

Exchanges: 3 1/2 Fat, 4 Vegetable, 3 Lean Protein, 1/2 Other Carbohydrate, 1 Starch 490 calories; carbohydrates 44.3g 14% DV; protein 31g 62% DV; exchange other carbs 3; sugars 14.9g; dietary fiber 7.9g 32% DV fat 21.7g 33% DV; sodium 653.1mg 26% DV cholesterol 73.7mg 25% DV; saturated fat 3.5g 18% DV; vitamin a iu 10972.2IU 219% DV; folate 127.3mcg 32% DV; vitamin c 54.3mg 91% DV calcium 88.3mg 9% DV; magnesium 114.2mg 41% DV; iron 3.3mg 18% DV; potassium 1240.4mg 35% DV.

LUNCH

Sheet-Pan Chicken and Vegetables with Romesco Sauce

A traditional Mediterranean sauce made of rusty peppers, nuts, garlic and olive oil, the Romesco wine is a wonderful mix of grilled beef, seafood, omelets and one-pan roast chicken meat and vegetables. All the roasted pumpkin, broccoli and chicken thighs make the fast, easy sauce for a quick and delicious one-starter meal.

Ingredients

- 2 large Yukon Gold potatoes, cubed
- 1 teaspoon ground pepper, divided
- 1 teaspoon paprika
- 4 tablespoons extra-virgin olive oil, divided
- ¼ cup slivered almonds
- ½ teaspoon salt, divided
- 4 cups broccoli florets

- 4 bone-in chicken thighs, skin removed, excess fat trimmed
- 1 (7 ounces) jar roasted red peppers, rinsed
- 1 small clove garlic, crushed
- 2 tablespoons chopped fresh cilantro for garnish
- ¼ teaspoon crushed red pepper
- ½ teaspoon ground cumin

Directions:

Step 1: Preheat 450 degrees F in the oven.

Step 2: Put potatoes in a medium bowl with 1/4 teaspoon pepper, one teaspoon oil and 1/8 teaspoon salt. Place a wide-rimmed baking sheet on one side. In the cup, 1/4 tea cubes place, one tablespoon oil, and 1/8 tea cubicle salt. Place on the baker's empty side. Fifteen minutes of roasting.

Step 3: In the meantime, add two tea cubes of oil, 1/4 tea cucumber of pepper and 1/8 tea cubicles of salt in a clean cup. After 10 minutes of roasting, add broccoli on the potato side of the baking sheet. Remove the vegetables and proceed to roast until chicken is cooked and the vegetables are tender, about 15 minutes longer.

Step 4: Meanwhile, in the mini food processor mix roasted peppers, almonds, paprika, garlic, cumin, pumped red pepper and rest of 2 tablespoon oil with 1/8 tea cubicle salt and also 1/4 tea cubicle pepper. Process up to smoothness.

Step 5: Serve with the roast pepper sauce chicken and vegetables. Sprinkle, if necessary, with cilantro.

Nutrition Facts

Serving Size: 1 Cup Vegetables, 1 Chicken Thigh, and 2 Tablespoons Sauce

Exchanges: 4 Lean Protein, 4 1/2 Fat, 1 1/2 Vegetable, 1 Starch 498.8 calories; carbohydrates 29.5g 10% DV; protein 33g 66% DV; exchange other carbs 2; sugars 2.2g; Fat 26.6g 41% DV; dietary fiber 4.5g 18% DV saturated fat 4.8g 24% DV; vitamin a iu 3096.1IU 62% DV; cholesterol 142.5mg 48% DV; vitamin c 75.1mg 125% DV; calcium 88.1mg 9% DV; iron 2.8mg 16% DV; folate 67.1mcg 17% DV; magnesium 81.4mg 29% DV sodium 664.6mg 27% DV; potassium 878.6mg 25% DV; thiamin 0.3mg 25% DV.

DINNER

Sheet-Pan Mediterranean Chicken, Brussels sprouts and Gnocchi

Chicken thighs, Cherry tomatoes and Brussels sprouts, packaged gnocchi are roasted on the same pot for the entire meal which cannot be made easier in this nutritious dinner. And although it is essential, this dish has loads of flavor, including garlic, oregano and red wine vinegar, coming from the Mediterranean. It's all applied to a dish ready for an intense weekend rotation in your kitchen.

Ingredients
- 4 tablespoons extra-virgin olive oil, divided
- 1 cup sliced red onion
- 4 boneless, skinless chicken thighs, trimmed
- 2 tablespoons chopped fresh oregano, divided
- ½ teaspoon ground pepper, divided
- 2 large cloves garlic, minced, divided
- ¼ teaspoon salt, divided
- 1-pound Brussels sprouts, trimmed and quartered
- 1 tablespoon red-wine vinegar
- 1 (16 ounces) package shelf-stable gnocchi
- 1 cup halved cherry tomatoes

Directions
Step 1
Preheat the oven to 450 ° F.
Step 2
In a large bowl, add two cubicles of oregano, 1/2 garlic, one tablespoon of oregano, 1/4 teaspoon of pepper and 1/8 teaspoon of salt. Add sprouts, gnocchi, and onion to Brussels and toss to cover. Spread over a large bakery.
Step 3
In the wide cup, add one tablespoon oregano, one tablespoon oil, remaining garlic and 1/4 tea cucumber and 1/8 tea cucumber salt. Attach chicken to cover and throw. Nestle the chicken into the mixture of vegetables—10 minutes of roasting.
Step 4

Remove from the oven and add tomatoes; blend with the mixture. Continue roasting until the sprouts are tender in Brussels and chicken just fried, about ten minutes longer. Stir the vinegar into the vegetable mixture and the remaining one tablespoon oil.

Nutrition Facts
Serving Size: 1 Chicken Thigh and 1 1/2 Cups Vegetables Each
Per Serving:
Exchanges: 2 1/2 Fat 3 Starch, 4 Lean Protein, 3 Vegetable,

DAY THREE
BREAKFAST

Ginger-Tahini Oven-Baked Salmon and Vegetables
In this balanced salmon recipe, the tahini sauce serves as a glaze for the fish, as well as a drizzle for the entire dish at the end of cooking. The green beans are only slightly cooked in this recipe, to stay crisp. If you like your tenderer green beans, look in the grocery store for thinner beans or bean greens; they'll cook more efficiently. It's not only delicious but also only 25 minutes of active cooking time, and afterwards, there's only one pan to clean up!

Ingredients
- 1 large, sweet potato, cubed (about 12 oz.)
- 2 tablespoons chopped fresh chives
- 1-pound white button or/and cremini mushrooms, cut into 1-inch pieces (6 cups)
- ½ teaspoon salt, divided
- 2 tablespoons olive oil, divided
- 1 tablespoon plus 2 tsp. tahini
- 1-pound green beans, trimmed
- 2 tablespoons reduced-sodium soy sauce
- 1 tablespoon plus 1 tsp. honey
- 1 ¼ pounds salmon, preferably wild-caught, cut into four portions
- 1 ½ teaspoons finely grated fresh ginger
- 2 teaspoons rice vinegar

Directions
Step 1: Put in the oven a wide-rimmed baker's pan. Place one rack in the Centre of the oven and another about 6 inches from the broiler. 425 degrees F. Preheat.

Step 2: Mix sweet potato, champagne, 1 tbsp. Gas, 1/4 of a tsp. Salt in a wide bowl; cover with the toss.

Step 3: Remove from the oven the bakery pan. Spread on the pot in one layer of the vegetable mixture, roast and stir until the sweet potatoes start browning for about 20 minutes.

Step 4: Meanwhile, throw the remaining 1 tbsp of green beans. Oil and a fifth of a tsp. Salt. Salt. In a small cup, mix soy sauce, tahini, honey and ginger.

Step 5: Take the pot out of the oven. Place the mushrooms and the sweet potatoes on the one hand and the green beans on the other. Place the salmon in the Centre, if need be, nestle them over the vegetables. Spread on the top of the salmon half of the tahini sauce. Roast for 8 to 10 minutes, before the salmon flakes. Switch the broiler high and move the pan to the top rack and broil for about three minutes until the salmon is glazed.

Step 6: Add vinegar and drizzle over salmon and vegetables into the remaining tahini sauce. Garnish with chives and serve if desired.

Nutrition Facts

Serving Size: 1 Piece Salmon + 1 3/4 Cups Vegetables

554.9 calories; carbohydrates 37.3g 12% DV; protein 37.7g 76% DV; exchange other carbs 2.5; sugars 15.6g; Fat 29.9g 46% DV; dietary fiber 7.6g 31% DV; saturated fat 5.9g 29% DV; vitamin a iu 13047IU 261% DV; cholesterol 78mg 26% DV; vitamin c 21.1mg 35% DV; calcium 102.6mg 10% DV; folate 112mcg 28% DV iron 2.8mg 15% DV; potassium 1387.7mg 39% DV; magnesium 101.7mg 36% DV; sodium 718.4mg 29% DV.

LUNCH

Charred Shrimp and Pesto Buddha Bowls

These Buddha shrimp and pesto bowls are tasty, balanced, lovely and take less than 30 minutes to prepare. In other words, they are practically the last simple dinner for the weekend. Feel free to add more vegetables and exchange shrimp for chicken, tofu, beef, or edamame.

Ingredients

- ⅓ cup prepared pesto
- 1 avocado, diced
- 2 tablespoons balsamic vinegar
- ½ teaspoon salt
- 2 cups cooked quinoa
- 1 tbsp olive oil

- ¼ tsp fresh pepper
- 1 pound large, deshelled shrimp
- 4 cups rocket leaves
- 1 cup halved cherry tomatoes

Directions

Step 1

In a large bowl, whisk pesto, oil, vinegar, pepper and salt. Drop four teaspoons from the mixture into a small tub.

Step 2

Heat over medium-high heat, a big cast-iron skillet. Add shrimp and cook, stirring until slightly charred, 4 to 5 minutes. Take a tray.

Step 3

Fill the vinaigrette with arugula and quinoa in the large bowl and coat. Divide the mixture into 4 cups. Top with onions, shrimp and avocado. Drizzle each bowl with one reserved pesto mixture tablespoon.

Nutrition Facts

Serving Size: 2 1/2 Cups

Exchanges: 1/2 Vegetable 3 Lean Protein, 4 Fat, 1 1/2 Starch, 429.4 calories; carbohydrates 29.3g 9% DV; protein 30.9g 62% DV; exchange other carbs 2; sugars 5g; fat 22g 34% DV; dietary fiber 7.2g 29% DV saturated fat 3.6g 18% DV; vitamin a iu 1125.6IU 23% DV; cholesterol 187.5mg 63% DV; vitamin c 14.4mg 24% DV; calcium 205.4mg 21% DV; iron 2.9mg 16% DV folate 108.9mcg 27% DV; magnesium 130.5mg 47% DV; sodium 571.4mg 23% DV; potassium 901.1mg 25% DV; thiamin 0.2mg 16% DV.

DINNER

Turkey Meatballs with Linguine and Fresh Tomato Sauce

Lean ground turkey is combined with fresh mushrooms, oats, garlic and spices for this balanced turkey meatball, a little parmesan cheese for a juicy, tasty and more fibery, fat-less than a standard version of beef and pork. Serve these wonderful meatballs with fresh tomato sauce over whole-grain pasta for a good take on spaghetti and meatballs, and hold the remaining things into   sandwiches.

Ingredients

- 1 teaspoon olive oil
- 1 egg, lightly beaten
- 3 cups sliced fresh button mushrooms (8 ounces)
- ⅓ cup quick-cooking rolled oats
- 3 cloves garlic, minced
- ½ teaspoon salt
- 2 teaspoons dried Italian seasoning, crushed
- 1 recipe Linguine with Fresh Tomato Sauce
- ¼ teaspoon ground pepper
- 1 ¼ pounds lean ground turkey
- ⅓ cup finely grated Parmesan cheese

Direction

Step 1: Preheat the oven by 400 ° F and Line the shallow foil bakery, cover the foil with cooking mist.

Step 2: Heat oil on low heat in the medium pot. Add champagne; cook, stirring periodically until all the liquid has evaporated tenderly, 8 to 10 minutes. Shift to the food processor the mushrooms; process until finely chopped.

Step 3: In a big bowl, oats, mix egg, parmesan, Italian seasoning, garlic, pepper and salt. Include the champagne and turkey, blend well. Place that meat mixture on a cutting board in a rectangle and cut it into 30 squares. Roll each square into a ball and placed the balls in a prepared pot 1/2 inch apart. Bake until the meatballs are not rose anymore and the inner temperature reaches 165 degrees F for around 12 to 15 minutes.

Step 4: Divide between 4 plates or shallow bowls the linguine and sauce. Top any serving with six balls of meat. (For another meal, reserve the remaining meatballs; see note.)

Nutrition Facts

Serving Size: 1 Cup Pasta and 6 Meatballs

Exchanges: 1 Fat 3 Vegetable, 3 Lean Protein, 2 1/2 Starch, 467 calories; carbohydrates 49.2g 16% DV; protein 36.3g 73% DV; exchange other carbs 3.5; sugars 8.8g; dietary fiber 7.6g 31% DV fat 16.1g 25% DV; cholesterol 111mg 37% DV; saturated fat 4.7g 23% DV; vitamin a iu 2245.3IU 45% DV; folate 76.1mcg 19% DV sodium 622.5mg 25% DV; vitamin c 61mg 102% DV; calcium 131.9mg 13% DV; magnesium 83.5mg 30% DV; iron 5.1mg 28% DV; potassium 907mg 25% DV; thiamin 0.3mg 29% DV.

DAY FOUR

BREAKFAST
Roasted Salmon with Smoky Chickpeas and Greens

You will get a dose of greens and green dressing at this balanced salmon meal! Down on six portions or more of dark leafy greens, a week will help keep your brain in shape. This dish includes the latest method of the Test Kitchen for the medication of chickpeas: spice and roast until crispy.

Ingredients

- 2 tablespoons extra-virgin olive oil, divided
- ¼ cup of water
- 1 ¼ pounds wild salmon, cut into four portions
- ½ teaspoon ground pepper, divided
- 1 tablespoon smoked paprika
- 1 (15 ounces) can no-salt-added chickpeas, rinsed
- 10 cups chopped kale
- ½ teaspoon salt, divided, plus a pinch
- ⅓ cup buttermilk
- ¼ cup mayonnaise
- ¼ cup chopped fresh chives and/or dill, plus more for garnish
- ¼ teaspoon garlic powder

Directions

Step 1: In the third top and middle of the oven, place racks; preheat 425 degrees F.

Step 2: In a medium cup, mix one tablespoon oil, paprika and 1/4 teaspoon salt. Put the chickpeas very thoroughly dry, then toss with the paprika mixture. Spread over a rimmed sheet of the bakery. On the upper rack, stirring twice, for 30 minutes, bake the chickpeas.

Step 3: Pure buttermilk in the mixer until creamy, mayonnaise, spices, 1/4 tea cucumber pepper and the garlic powder. Put aside. Set aside.

Step 4: Heat the one tablespoon oil remaining over medium heat in a large pot. Attach the kale and cook for 2 minutes, stirring occasionally. Add water and cook until it's tender, about 5 minutes longer. Take off the heat and apply a pinch of salt.

Step 5: Take the chickpeas out of the oven and shift them to one side of the pot. Put salmon on the other side and season each salt and potato with the remaining 1/4 teaspoon. Bake for 5 to 8 minutes until salmon is just cooked.

Step 6: Drizzle reserved salmon dressing add more herbs, if needed, and serve with chickpeas and kale.

Nutrition Facts

Serving Size: 3/4 Cup Greens, 4 Oz. Salmon, 2 1/2 Tbsp. & 1/4 Cup Chickpeas.

Exchanges: 1 Starch, 5 Lean Protein, 1/2 Vegetable, 3 Fat 446.5 calories; carbohydrates 23.4g 8% DV; protein 37g 74% DV; exchange other carbs 1.5; sugars 2.2g; Fat 21.8g 34% DV; dietary fiber 6.4g 26% DV saturated fat 3.7g 19% DV; vitamin a iu 5200IU 104% DV; cholesterol 72.9mg 24% DV; vitamin c 51.7mg 86% DV; calcium 197.8mg 20% DV folate 77.9mcg 20% DV; Iron 3mg 17% DV; potassium 990.8mg 28% DV; magnesium 99.4mg 36% DV; sodium 556.7mg 22% DV.

LUNCH

Jackfruit Barbacoa Burrito Bowls

The jackfruit, tropical fruit with a thick, chewy structure, is a white, flavored canvas. The jackfruit is cooked in the vegetable bowls of the burrito in a soft, spicy chili sauce so that you will never know that you eat a plant protein instead of pork or beef.

Ingredients

- 2 tablespoons olive oil
- 6 garlic cloves, crushed
- 1 cup chopped white onion
- 1 ½ cups unsalted vegetable broth
- 1 medium New Mexico chili, stem and seeds removed
- 1 lime, quartered
- 2 (20 ounces) cans green jackfruit in brine, rinsed and shredded
- ½ teaspoon kosher salt
- 1 teaspoon chili powder
- ½ teaspoon ground pepper
- 1 cup unsalted canned black beans, rinsed
- 3 cups hot cooked brown rice
- 1 bay leaf
- 2 cups thinly sliced iceberg lettuce
- 1 ⅓ cups chopped plum tomatoes (about 3 medium)

• ½ cup chopped fresh cilantro

Directions

Step 1: Heat oil over medium-high heat in a medium saucepan. Add garlic, chili, onion and cook for about 6 minutes, whispering periodically until the onion is tender and browned. Add broth; heat up and bring to a boil. Cover partly and reduce heat to medium. Cook about 10 minutes until the chili is tender. Move the mix to a mixer. Remove the middle mixer lid piece (so that steam escapes); lock the lid on the mixer. Place a clean towel about 45 seconds through the opening and operation. (Pay attention when mixing hot liquids.)

Step 2: Return chili to the casserole with jackfruit, powdered salt, chili, laurels and pepper. Bring over medium-high heat to a cooker. Reduce the heat too from medium-low, cover, and cook for 6 to 8 minutes until slightly thicker. Remove the bay leaf.

Step 3: In each of 4 shallow bowls, put 3/4 of a cup of rice. Cover each one with a mixture of 1/2 cup salad, 3/4 cup Jackfruit, 1/3 cup tomatoes, 2 cups of coriander and 1/4 cup beans. Serve with wedges of lime.

Nutrition Facts

Serving Size: 1 Bowl

450.1 calories; carbohydrates 80.3g 26% DV; protein 9.6g 19% DV; exchange other carbs 5.5; sugars 6.1g; fat 9.4g 14% DV; dietary fiber 22.1g 89% DV saturated fat 1.4g 7% DV; vitamin c 41.3mg 69% DV; vitamin a iu 3019.1IU 60% DV; folate 66.5mcg 17% DV; iron 4.1mg 23% DV; calcium 178.2mg 18% DV; magnesium 109mg 39% DV; sodium 755.5mg 30% DV; potassium 612.5mg 17% DV; thiamin 0.3mg 35% DV.

DINNER
Chicken, Quinoa and Sweet Potato Casserole

This protein-powered chicken and sweet potato saucepan is made from multicolored quinoa, a combination of blue, red and black, but any color works.

Ingredients

- 3 tablespoons water
- 4 cups cubed peeled sweet potatoes (about 1 pound)
- 1 tablespoon canola oil
- 2 cups chopped seeded poblano chilies
- 1 ½ pounds boneless, skinless chicken thighs, trimmed
- ½ cup thinly sliced shallots
- 2 cups unsalted chicken broth
- 1 ½ cups multi colored quinoa
- ½ cup crumbled queso fresco
- 2 tablespoons minced garlic
- ⅓ cup dry white wine
- ½ teaspoon ground cinnamon
- 1 teaspoon kosher salt
- 1 teaspoon ground cumin
- ⅛ teaspoon cayenne pepper
- ¼ cup fresh cilantro

Directions

Step 1: Preheat the oven to 400 F.

Step 2: In a bowl, put sweet potatoes and water. Plastic wrap cover; pierce a few holes with a fork in the end. Microwave 4 minutes on Heavy.

Step 3: In the meantime, heat oil over medium-high heat in a large saucepan. Add chicken and cook 4 to 5 minutes per side until browned. Switch the chicken to a clean cutting board and allow 5 minutes to stand. Split into strips of 1 inch.

Step 4: Put into the pan and stir until the shallots are lightly browned about 2 minutes, and cook over medium-high, stirring occasionally. Stir in bread, quinoa, wine, salt, cumin and cayenne. Bring to boil. Bring to boil. Remove from heat and add chicken and sweet potatoes.

Step 5: Spoon the mixture into a broiler-resistant 7-by-11-inch (or equivalent size). Cover with foil, cover with foil. Twenty minutes of baking.

Step 6: Remove from the oven; now raise the temperature of an oven to barbecue. Sprinkle the casserole with cheese. Broil about 5 minutes from the heat source until golden brown. Sprinkle cilantro with the sprinkler. Let cool before serving for 5 minutes.

Nutrition Facts
Serving Size: 1 Cup
Exchanges: 2 1/2 Starch, 1/2 Fat, 2 Lean Protein, 1/2 Vegetable 349.3 calories; carbohydrates 38.7g 13% DV; protein 22.9g 46% DV; exchange other carbs 2.5; sugars 5.7g; Fat 10.5g 16% DV dietary fiber 5.3g 21% DV; saturated fat 2.7g 14% DV; vitamin an iu 9751IU 195% DV; cholesterol 83.3mg 28% DV; vitamin c 13.8mg 23% DV; calcium 95.9mg 10% DV; folate 73.3mcg 18% DV Iron 3mg 17% DV; potassium 659.6mg 19% DV; magnesium 99.3mg 36% DV; sodium 431.8mg 17% DV.

DAY FIVE

BREAKFAST
Paprika Baked Pork Tenderloin with Potatoes and Broccoli
You can never picture this elegant meal on just one baking sheet. While the pork rests, fill this impressive, balanced dinner with a simple red pepper sauce. The sauce with chicken is also delicious. We are ready to bet on this simple pan dinner recipe to go into heavy rotation on the playlist of your kitchen.

Ingredients
• ¾ pound Yukon Gold potatoes, scrubbed and cut into 1-inch pieces
• 2 cloves garlic, peeled
• 1 medium red onion, cut into 1-inch pieces
• 2 tablespoons olive oil, divided
• 2 jarred roasted red bell peppers (6 oz.)
• 1 teaspoon lemon juice

• 2 tablespoons low-fat plain Greek yogurt or low-fat sour cream
• 4 cups broccoli florets (about 1 lb.)
• 1 ½ teaspoons smoked paprika
• ½ teaspoon ground pepper, divided
• ¾ teaspoon salt, divided
• 1 (1 pound) pork tenderloin, trimmed
• 2 teaspoons Dijon mustard

Directions

Step 1: In the oven, placed a large baker's rimmed sheet; preheat to 425 ° F.

Step 2: Combine ointment, potatoes, 1 dc. Gas, 1/4 of a tsp. Medium bowl salt; coat toss. Remove the pot from the oven; cover with spray for cooking. Spread the mixture of potatoes on the bowl; roast 15 minutes.

Step 3: In the meantime, mix 2 tsp broccoli. Olive oil, 1/4 of a centimeter. Medium bowl salt; coat toss. On a small piece of foil, put garlic. Drizzle with 1 tsp left. Petroleum; fold in a small envelope. Combine 1/4 tsp. Paprika, ground pepper and 1/4 tsp left. In a tiny tub, salt. Spread mustard over pork. Coat with the mixture of paprika.

Step 4: Take the pot out of the oven. Remove the potatoes and onions to one side. Next to the potatoes put the pork; scatter the broccoli over the plate. Place the garlic packet where space is available. Roast until an instant reading thermometer in the thickest part of the pork registers is 145 degrees F, approximately 25 minutes.

Step 5: Enable the pork to rest while making the sauce: unwrap the garlic carefully and move it to a mini food processor or blender. Add roasted red peppers, sour cream (or yoghurt), lemon juice and 1/4 tsp. Rest. Ground pepper and puree until soft.

Step 6: Swallow the pork in 12 slices. Divide between 4 plates pork, beans, and broccoli. Drizzle over the end, the red pepper sauce.

Nutrition Facts

322.6 calories; carbohydrates 28.7g 9% DV; protein 30g 60% DV; exchange other carbs 2; sugars 5.5g; Fat 10.3g 16% DV dietary fiber 5.3g 21% DV; saturated fat 2.1g 10% DV; cholesterol 76.2mg 25% DV; vitamin a iu 3879.9IU 78% DV; potassium 1246.8mg 35% DV; vitamin c 154mg 257% DV; folate 98.4mcg 25% DV iron 3.2mg 18% DV; calcium 98.9mg 10% DV; magnesium 83.8mg 30% DV; sodium 730.7mg 29% DV.

LUNCH

Creamy Chicken, Brussels sprouts and Mushrooms One-Pot Pasta

In this simple pasta, you just have to dirty one pot, cook chicken and vegetables along with the noodles. In addition, the starch which is typically drained with pasta water remains in the pot by using the same amount of water that you need to cook the pasta, giving you deliciously creamy results.

Ingredients

- 8 ounces' whole-wheat linguine or spaghetti
- 4 cups water
- ¾ teaspoon dried rosemary
- 2 tablespoons chopped fresh chives
- 1-pound boneless, skinless chicken thighs
- 2 cups sliced Brussels sprouts
- 4 cups sliced mushrooms
- 1 ¼ teaspoons dried thyme
- 1 medium onion, chopped
- 4 cloves garlic, thinly sliced
- 2 tablespoons Boursin cheese
- ¾ teaspoon salt

Directions

Step 1: In a big pot, mix pasta, chicken, champagne, Brussels sprouts, onion, garlic, torsion, thyme, rosemary and salt. Remove in the bath. Get high heat to a boil. Boil, stirring regularly until the pasta has been cooked and the water has almost evaporated, for 10 to 12 minutes. Remove it from heat then let it stand for 5 minutes, stirring occasionally. Serve with chives scattered.

Nutrition

Serving: About 1 1/2 Cups Each

Exchanges: 1 1/2 Vegetable, 2 1/2 Starch, 2 1/2 Lean Meat 352.5 calories; carbohydrates 41.7g 14% DV; protein 27g 54% DV; exchange other carbs 3; dietary fiber 7.6g 30% DV; saturated fat 3.6g 18% DV; sugars 4.4g; Fat 10.3g 16% DV cholesterol 67.4mg 23% DV; niacin equivalents 8.8mg 68% DV; vitamin an iu 354.8IU 7% DV; vitamin b6 0.4mg 25% DV; folate 68.6mcg 17% DV; vitamin c 27.6mg 46% DV; calcium 63.4mg 6% DV; magnesium 97.3mg 35% DV; iron 3.8mg 21% DV; potassium 567.5mg 16% DV; thiamin 0.3mg 30% DV; sodium 460.9mg 18% DV; percent of calories from protein 29;percent of calories from carbs 45; calories from fat 92.4kcal; percent of calories from fat 25; percent of calories from sat fat 8.

DINNER
Family-Style Chicken Spaghetti
Serves 4 (serving size: 2 cups)
Ingredients

- 2 teaspoons olive oil
- 8 ounces uncooked whole-wheat spaghetti
- 2 pt. cherry tomatoes
- 3 garlic cloves, smashed
- 1/4 cup fresh basil leaves, divided
- 1 medium onion, cut into 1-in. wedges
- 1/2 teaspoon kosher salt
- 2 tablespoons unsalted tomato paste
- 8 ounces shredded skinless, boneless rotisserie chicken breast (about 2 cups)
- 1/2 teaspoon freshly ground black pepper
- 3 tablespoons shaved Parmesan cheese

Preparation
Step 1 —— Preheat your broiler. Line the foil with a jelly-roll pan.

Step 2 — Cook the pasta, omitting salt and fat, according to package instructions.

Step 3 — Combine the oil, garlic, tomatoes, and onion in a prepared pan while the pasta is cooking; toss. Broil for 4-6 minutes. Move the mixture from the pan and any liquid to a blender. Add two tablespoons of basil and tomato paste; put the lid on the blender firmly. Remove the middle of the blender lid from the center; cover with a kitchen towel. Blend until perfectly smooth.

Step 4 — Pasta drain; return to plate. Combine the tomato sauce, salt, chicken, and pepper. Until hot, cook over medium heat. Place the mixture of spaghetti on a serving platter. The remaining two tablespoons of basil leaves are chopped. Sprinkle evenly with basil and parmesan over spaghetti.

Nutritional Information

- Calories 404
- Satfat 2.1g
- Fat 7.5g
- Polyfat 1.1g
- Monofat 3.3g
- Carbohydrate 55g
- Protein 34g
- Cholesterol 70mg
- Fiber 10g
- Sodium 603mg

- Iron 3mg
- Sugars 9g
- Calcium 137mg
- Est. added sugars 0g

DAY SIX

BREAKFAST
Family-Style Meatball "Fondue"
Active Time - 30 Mins
Total Time - 30 Mins
Serves 4 (serving size: 6 bread slices, 6 meatballs, and about 1/2 cup sauce)
Ingredients
- 3/4 cup chopped zucchini
- Cooking spray
- 1/3 cup chopped yellow onion
- 12 ounces ground turkey
- 1/4 teaspoon kosher salt
- 1/2 teaspoon dried oregano
- 1 large egg
- 1/4 teaspoon black pepper
- 8 ounces sliced cremini mushrooms
- 1 tablespoon olive oil
- 1 1/2 cups low-salt marinara sauce
- 2 garlic cloves, minced
- 4 ounces, shredded and reduced-fat mozzarella
- 1/4 cup water
- 24 thin slices from a whole-wheat baguette, toasted

Preparation
Step 1- Preheat the oven to 400 degrees F. Line an aluminum foil baking sheet; cover with cooking spray.

Step 2 — Place the zucchini between the paper towels in a double layer; squeeze to remove excess moisture. In a dish, combine the zucchini, turkey, onion, oregano, salt, pepper, and egg together. Shape 24 meatballs, about one tablespoon each, with turkey mixture; place on prepared baking sheets. (Turkey mixture will be very soft, but as meatballs cook, it firms up.) Bake at 400 ° F, about 12 minutes, until fully cooked.

Step 3 — meanwhile, heat a big, medium-high ovenproof skillet. In a pan, add oil; swirl to coat. Add the mushrooms and garlic; cook until the mushroom liquid is mostly evaporated, occasionally stirring, around 5 minutes. Stir in 1/4 cup of the water and marinara sauce; reduce heat to low, and simmer for 5 minutes. Return the meatballs to the saucepan (leave the cooked-out proteins behind); swirl gently to cover with the sauce. Sprinkle with cheese on an even basis.

Step 4 — Preheat the broiler with the top-position oven rack. Broil the meatball mixture for about 2 minutes, until the cheese is melted and bubbly. Serve with baguette toast.

Nutritional Information

- Calories 403
- Satfat 6g
- Fat 21g
- Protein 31g
- Unsatfat 12g
- Fiber 3g
- Added sugars g
- Carbohydrate 26g
- Calcium 26% DV
- Sodium 693mg
- Sugars 7g
- Potassium 15% DV

LUNCH
Sesame-Ginger-Chickpea-Stuffed Sweet Potatoes
Active Time - 40 Mins

Total Time - 1 Hour 40 Mins

Serves 4 (serving size: 2 stuffed sweet potato halves)

Ingredients

- 1 teaspoon canola oil
- 4 medium sweet potatoes (about 8 oz.)
- 2 teaspoons toasted sesame oil
- 1 (15-oz.) can unsalted chickpeas, rinsed and drained
- 1/2 teaspoon kosher salt, divided
- 1 teaspoon garlic powder
- 3 tablespoons tahini, well stirred
- 1/2 teaspoon ground ginger
- 1 teaspoon grated fresh garlic
- 1 teaspoon grated peeled fresh ginger
- 3 tablespoons hot water
- 1 teaspoon rice vinegar
- 2 teaspoons water
- 4 teaspoons Sriracha chili sauce
- 1/2 tsp. white and black sesame seeds
- 1/4 cup thinly sliced green onions

Preparation

Step 1 – Preheat the oven to 400 degrees F.

Step 2 — Rub canola oil on the potatoes; pierce liberally with a fork. Bake for 1 hour at 400 ° F or until tender. Nice. Great. Split the potatoes lengthwise in half. Score the flesh softly with the tip of your knife.

Step 3 — Place on a baking sheet with the chickpeas; pat dry with paper towels. Sesame oil, add; toss. Sprinkle with 1/4 teaspoon salt, garlic powder, and ground ginger; toss. Bake for 30 minutes at 400 ° F, stirring every 10 minutes.

Step 4 — In a cup, combine the tahini, fresh garlic, fresh ginger, and vinegar together. Add three tablespoons of hot water; mix until smooth and loose.

Step 5 — In a cup, combine the Sriracha and two teaspoons of water. Sprinkle about two teaspoons of tahini mixture over each half of the sweet potato; top with 1/4 of the remaining teaspoon of salt. Top with the mixture of chickpeas, the remaining mixture of tahini, the mixture of Sriracha, green onions, and sesame seeds.

Nutritional Information

- Calories 413
- Satfat 1.3g
- Fat 10.6g
- Polyfat 4.1g
- Monofat 4.1g
- Carbohydrate 69g
- Protein 12g
-
- Cholesterol 0.0mg
- Fiber 12g
- Sodium 495mg
- Iron 3mg
- Sugars 10g
- Calcium 136mg
- Est. added sugars 1g

DINNER

Greek Chopped Salad with Grilled Pita

Active Time - 30 Mins

Total Time - 30 Mins

Serves 4 (serving size: about 2 1/4 cups salad and about 4 pita wedges)

Ingredients

- 1 large red bell pepper
- Cooking spray

- 2 teaspoons chopped fresh oregano, divided

- 1/4 cup olive oil, divided
- 3/8 teaspoon kosher salt, divided
- 1/2 teaspoon garlic powder
- 1 tablespoon white wine vinegar
- 3 (6 1/2-in.) whole-wheat pita rounds
- 2 teaspoons Dijon mustard
- 1 tablespoon fresh lemon juice
- 4 cups chopped romaine lettuce
- 1/4 teaspoon black pepper
- 1 cup halved cherry tomatoes
- 2 cups chopped English cucumber
- 1 (15-oz.) can unsalted cannellini beans, rinsed and drained
- 2 tablespoons pitted kalamata olives, chopped
- 1-ounce feta cheese, crumbled (about 1/4 cup)

Preparation

Step 1 — Heat a medium-high barbecue plate. Cover pan with spray for cooking. Remove the bell pepper seeds and membranes; cut them into pieces. Add bell pepper to the pan; cook on each side for 4 minutes or until soft and charred. Remove the bell pepper from the pan; cut into pieces that are bite-size.

Step 2 — In a cup, mix 1 tablespoon of olive oil, 1 teaspoon of oregano, powdered garlic, and 1/8 teaspoon of salt. Brush the mixture of oil uniformly over all pita rounds on both sides. Add the pita rounds to the pan; cook on each side for 2 minutes or until marked well. Slice each pita into six wedges.

Step 3 — In just a wide bowl, mix the remaining 3 tablespoons of oil, vinegar, juice, and mustard and stir with a whisk. Stir in 1 teaspoon of oregano remaining, 1/4 teaspoon of salt remaining, and black pepper. Combine the bowl with the lettuce, charred red bell pepper, tomatoes, cucumber, olives, and beans; toss well. Divide the salad into four dishes; blend equally with the cheese. Serve with wedges of grilled pita.

Nutritional Information

- Calories 396
- Satfat 3g
- Fat 19g
- Protein 12g
- Unsatfat 12g
- Fiber 10g
- Carbohydrate 48g
- Calcium 12% DV
- Sodium 684mg
- Sugars 6g

- Potassium 21% DV
- Added sugars 0g

DAY SEVEN

BREAKFAST
Tangy Chicken-Farro Bowl

Serves 4 (serving size: 3/4 cup farro, 3 ounces chicken, 3 tablespoons pickles, 1 tablespoon preserves, and 1 tablespoon dressing)

Ingredients

- 2 tablespoons sugar, divided
- 5 tablespoons white vinegar, divided
- 1/8 teaspoon ground allspice
- 5/8 teaspoon kosher salt, divided
- 2 tablespoons Dijon mustard
- 2 Persian cucumbers, thinly sliced
- 1 tablespoon canola oil
- 1/2 teaspoon dry mustard
- 2 (8.5-ounce) packages precooked farro
- 2 teaspoons finely chopped fresh dill
- 1/4 cup lingonberry preserves
- 2 (6-ounce) skinless, boneless rotisserie chicken breasts, sliced

Preparation

Step 1 —— In a dish, add 1/4 cup of vinegar, four teaspoons of sugar, 1/4 teaspoon of salt, and allspice; whisk together. Stir in the cucumbers, toss. Let stand for 12 minutes until thrown. Uh, drain.

Step 2 — Combine the Dijon mustard, the dry mustard, the oil, the remaining one tablespoon of vinegar, and the remaining two teaspoons of sugar in a bowl. Stir in the water with the dill and 1 1/2 teaspoons.

Step 3 —— Heat Farro as per package instructions. Divide them into four bowls. Arrange the chicken, cucumbers, and farro with preserves. Sprinkle with mustard sauce; apply the remaining 3/8 of a teaspoon of salt.

Nutritional Information

- Calories 406
- Satfat 1.2g
- Fat 7.6g
- Polyfat 1.6g
- Monofat 3.3g
- Carbohydrate 53g

- Protein 31g
- Est. added sugars 15g
- Cholesterol 72mg
- Fiber 4g
- Sodium 371mg
- Iron 3mg
- Sugars 16g
- Calcium 44mg

LUNCH
Dilly Salmon Packets with Asparagus
Serves 4 (serving size: 1 fillet and 4 oz. asparagus)
Ingredients
- 4 (6-oz.) salmon fillets (about 1-in. thick)
- Cooking spray
- 1/4 cup chopped fresh dill
- 2 tablespoons unsalted butter
- 1/2 teaspoon black pepper
- 1/2 teaspoon kosher salt
- 2 tablespoons olive oil
- 8 orange slices
- 1-pound asparagus, trimmed

Preparation
Step 1— Preheat the grill to a medium-high temperature.

Step 2 — Coat 4 (12-inch-square) cooking spray pieces of foil; place one fillet in the center of each piece. Add 1 1/2 teaspoons of butter and one tablespoon of dill to each fillet. With salt, pepper, and orange slices, top evenly. Bring the foil edges over the fillets; fold to seal. Place the packets on the grill, seal side up, cover, and grill for 12 minutes or until the degree of doneness is desired. Remove bundles of foil from the grill.

Step 3 —Combine in a bowl with oil and asparagus; toss. Place the asparagus on the grill; grill for 5 minutes or until crisp, turning once for 3 minutes. Divide the asparagus evenly between the four dishes. Open packets; top with fillets of asparagus. Squeeze slices of orange evenly over the fillets.

Nutritional Information
- Calories 394
- Satfat 6.3g
- Fat 23.6g
- Polyfat 5.3g
- Monofat 10g
- Carbohydrate 9g
- Protein 37g
- Est. added sugars 0g
- Cholesterol 109mg
- Fiber 3g

- Sodium 319mg
- Iron 4mg
- Sugars 5g
- Calcium 67mg

DINNER
Provolone and Broccoli Rabe Beef Sliders
Total Time - 20 Mins
Serves 4 (serving size: 2 sliders)
Ingredients
- 7 ounces broccoli, trimmed
- Cooking spray
- 1 tablespoon extra-virgin olive oil
- 1 1/2 tablespoons red wine vinegar
- 1 pound 93% lean ground sirloin
- 1 teaspoon sugar
- 1/2 teaspoon Worcestershire sauce
- 1 teaspoon smoked paprika
- 1/4 teaspoon freshly ground black pepper
- 1/4 teaspoon kosher salt
- 8 (1-oz.) whole-wheat slider buns
- 3 (1-oz.) slices reduced-fat provolone cheese, torn into small pieces
- 8 heirloom tomato slices

Preparation
Step 1 — Heat a medium-high barbecue plate. Cover pan with spray for cooking. Add the broccoli; cook for 5 minutes, sometimes turning. Chop coarsely. In a small cup, add the vinegar, oil, and sugar. Add the broccoli; toss.

Step 2 — In a tub, combine the beef, paprika, Worcestershire, salt, and pepper together. Form into eight patties (3-inch-wide).

Step 3 — Back to the medium-high pan. Cover pan with spray for cooking. Apply the pan to the patties; cook for 2 to 3 minutes. Switch; cook for 1 to 2 minutes. Top with cheese patties; cover and cook for 1 minute or until the cheese has melted.

Step 4 — On the bottom half of each bun, place one patty; top with tomato, broccoli mixture, and top bun halves.

Nutritional Information
- Calories 404
- Satfat 4.8g

- Fat 15.9g
- Polyfat 2.5g
- Monofat 6.3g
- Carbohydrate 32g
- Protein 38g
- Cholesterol 71mg

- Fiber 2g
- Sodium 573mg
- Iron 4mg
- Est. added sugars 6
- Calcium 261mg
- Sugars 7

WEEK TWO

DAY ONE

BREAKFAST
BBQ Chicken with Peach and Feta Slaw
Serves 4 (serving size: 1 1/2 cups slaw and about 3 1/2 oz. chicken)
Ingredients

- 2 tablespoons sherry vinegar
- 5 tablespoons olive oil, divided
- 3/8 tsp. kosher salt, divided
- 1/2 tsp. freshly ground black pepper, divided
- 1 (12-oz.) pkg. broccoli slaw
- 2 center-cut bacon slices, cooked and crumbled

- 1 1/2 cups sliced fresh peaches
- 1/4 cup barbecue sauce
- 3 (6-oz.) skinless, boneless chicken breasts, cut crosswise into 1-in. strips
- 1-ounce feta cheese, crumbled (about 1/4 cup)
- 1 tablespoon chopped fresh chives

Preparation
Step 1- Combine in a large bowl, stirring with a fork, 4 tsp. oil, vinegar, 1/4 tsp. pepper, and 1/4 teaspoon salt. Apply the peaches and slaw to the mixture of vinegar; toss to cover gently.

Step 2 — Sprinkle the chicken with 1/4 of the remaining teaspoon of pepper and 1/8 of the remaining teaspoon of salt. Heat the remaining one tablespoon of the oil over the medium to high heat in a large non-stick skillet.

Place the chicken in the pan and cook for 6 minutes or until finished. Put your chicken in a big bowl. Add the bowl of barbecue sauce; toss.

Step 3 — Divide the slaw mixture equally between 4 plates; top with the chicken strips equally. Using chives, feta, and bacon to sprinkle.

Nutritional Information

- Fat 22.5g
- Calories 407
- Monofat 13.7g
- Satfat 4.4g
- Protein 33g
- Polyfat 2.4g
- Fiber 3g
- Carbohydrate 16g
- Iron 2mg
- Cholesterol 90mg
- Calcium 67mg
- Sodium 631mg
- Est. added sugars 5g
- Sugars 10g

LUNCH
Mini Veggie Tlayudas
Active Time - 45 Mins
Total Time - 1 Hour 10 Mins
Serves 6 (serving size: 1 tlayuda
Ingredients

- 2 tablespoons olive oil
- 1 cup hulled pumpkin seeds (pepitas)
- 1 garlic clove, minced
- 1 teaspoon ground cumin
- 1/8 teaspoon freshly ground black pepper
- 1/8 teaspoon salt
- 1/4 cup chopped fresh cilantro
- 1 cup thinly sliced cabbage
- 6 (6-in.) corn tortillas
- 2 tablespoons fresh lime juice
- 4 ounces shredded Oaxaca cheese or reduced-fat mozzarella
- 1 1/2 cups soaked, then fried black beans
- 1 cup sliced tomatoes
- Cooking spray
- 1 large avocado, thinly sliced

Preparation

Step 1— Preheat a low grill.

Step 2 — Over low heat, heat a small skillet. Add the seeds to the pan; grill the seeds for 3 minutes or until lightly browned, stirring often. Place in a spice grinder or mini food processor; process until a coarse paste develops.

Step 3 — Over medium-high heat, heat a medium skillet. Use oil to add; swirl to coat. Apply the seeds, cumin, and garlic to the ground pumpkin; cook for 3 minutes or until fragrant. Stir in the pepper and salt.

Step 4 — In a medium cup, mix the cabbage, cilantro, and juice; toss well.

Step 5 — Arrange the tortillas in a single layer on a baking sheet lined with foil. Place the pan on the grill; grill for about 3 minutes before the tortillas begin to crisp.

Step 6 — Divide the paste of pumpkin seeds equally between the tortillas, spreading to an even layer. Spoon over each tortilla with approximately 1/4 cup of refried beans. With about 2 1/2 tablespoons of cheese, cover each tortilla. Place tortillas coated with cooking spray on the grill rack; grill for 5 minutes or until the cheese melts and the tortilla edges are crisp and browned.

Step 7 —Top with cuts of slaw, onion, and avocado.

Nutritional Information

- Calories 390
- Satfat 5.3g
- Fat 24.6g
- Polyfat 6.2g
- Monofat 11g
- Carbohydrate 26g
- Protein 18g
- Cholesterol 10mg
- Fiber 9g
- Sodium 299mg
- Iron 6mg
- Sugars 2g
- Calcium 226mg
- Est. added sugars 0g

DAY TWO

BREAKFAST
Honey-Ginger Glazed Salmon
Hands-on Time - 30 Mins
Total Time - 30 Mins
Serves 4 (serving size: 1 fillet, 1/2 cup rice, and 2 1/4 tsp. marinade)
Ingredients
- 1/2 cup honey
- Cooking spray
- 1 (1 1/2-inch) finely cut, fresh ginger
- 1/4 cup lower-sodium soy sauce
- 4 (6-ounce) salmon fillets
- 1 garlic clove, grated
- 2 cups cooked brown rice

Preparation
Step 1 – Preheat the oven to 400 degrees. Line an aluminum foil jelly-roll pan; gently brush the foil with the cooking spray.

Step 2 — Combine the honey and the next three ingredients over medium heat in a small saucepan; simmer for 2 minutes, stirring frequently. Refrigerate the marinade at room temperature.

Step 3 — In an 8-inch square glass or ceramic baking dish, put the fillets. Pour the cooled marinade over the fillets, turning to coat each one thoroughly. Let it stand for ten minutes.

Step 4 — To the prepared plate, move the fillets. Strain the marinade into a small saucepan through a sieve; discard the solids. Over the medium heat, bring the marinade to a simmer; cook for 5 minutes. In a small bowl, reserve two tablespoons of marinade, and in a separate small bowl, reserve three tablespoons. Discard any marinade that remains.

Step 5 — Roast the fillets for 5 minutes at 400 °; remove the pan from the oven.

Step 6 — Preheat the broiler to a high degree.

Step 7 — Brush fillets with two tablespoons reserved marinade; broil on top for 1 to 2 minutes or until fillets are done and glazed. Serve over the rice fillets; drizzle with the remaining three tablespoons of marinade.

Nutritional Information

- Calories 408
- Satfat 2.2g
- Fat 10.4g
- Polyfat 3.6g
- Monofat 3.5g
- Carbohydrate 38g
- Protein 39g

- Cholesterol 90mg
- Fiber 2g
- Sodium 299mg
- Iron 1mg
- Sugars 15g
- Calcium 30mg
- Est. added sugars 15g

LUNCH
Cherry Tomato Pasta with Prosciutto and Asiago

Hands-on Time - 23 Mins

Total Time - 23 Mins

Serves 4 (serving size: 1 3/4 cups)

Ingredients

- 3 tablespoons olive oil, divided
- 8 ounces uncooked whole-grain penne or rotini
- 1 cup chopped red onion
- 1 ounce thinly sliced prosciutto, coarsely chopped
- 1/8 teaspoon crushed red pepper
- 8 garlic cloves, thinly sliced
- 3 cups multicolored cherry tomatoes, halved
- 1 medium zucchini, quartered lengthwise and sliced
- 2 teaspoons balsamic vinegar
- 1/2 teaspoon kosher salt
- 2 ounces Asiago cheese, grated and divided (about 1/2 cup)
- 1/3 cup chopped fresh flat-leaf parsley

Preparation

Step 1— Cook pasta according to the instructions for the package; drain.

Step 2 — Heat 1 tablespoon of oil over medium to high heat in a large skillet. Add prosciutto; cook until crisp, or 3 minutes. Remove the prosciutto from the casserole. To the tub, apply the remaining two tablespoons of oil. Garnish with onion, garlic, and pepper and sauté for 4 minutes. Stir in the zucchini;

cook for 1 minute. Add salt and tomatoes; cook for 3 minutes. Stir in the vinegar and pasta; cook for 30 seconds. Take the pan off the heat; add the parsley and 1 ounce of cheese. Divide the pasta mixture into four bowls; top with the prosciutto and 1 ounce of cheese remaining.

Nutritional Information

- Calories 405
- Satfat 4.3g
- Fat 17.3g
- Polyfat 2.5g
- Monofat 9.1g
- Carbohydrate 53g
- Protein 15g

- Cholesterol 17mg
- Fiber 8g
- Sodium 499mg
- Iron 3mg
- Sugars 11g
- Calcium 149mg
- Est. added sugars 0g

DINNER

Sheet Pan Balsamic Chicken and Vegetables

Preparation Time: 10 Minutes
Cooking Time: 20 Minutes
Serving: 4

Ingredients

- ·

- 1.33 lbs. boneless skinless chicken breast
- · 2 cups mushrooms, halved
- · 2 carrots, sliced
- · 1 red onion, sliced thin
- · 1 red bell pepper, sliced thin
- · 1 tbsp Italian seasoning (more to taste)

- · 1 tbsp. olive oil
- · 2 cups cherry tomatoes
- · 1 green bell pepper, sliced thin
- · 4 garlic cloves, minced
- · 2 tbsp balsamic vinegar (more to taste)
- · Salt and pepper

Preparation

- The oven should be preheated to 425 degrees.
- Pound the chicken so that it is about 1/2 inch thick. This will guarantee that it cooks uniformly and rapidly. A simple way to do this is by putting

and gently pounding the chicken between two sheets of plastic wrap. You can also have very thick chicken breasts with butterflies.

- Toss the balsamic vinegar, olive oil, Italian seasoning, garlic, salt, and pepper with the vegetables and chicken. Spread out flat on 1-2 baking sheets wrapped in foil and sprinkle with cooking spray. Make sure there is a single layer, and on top of each other, the chicken and vegetables are not stacked up.
- Bake until the chicken is cooked and the veggies are browned and soft, for 18-20 minutes.

Nutrition

Calories 286, Polyunsaturated Fat 0g, Saturated Fat 1g, Cholesterol 74mg, Total Fat 5g, Sodium 98mg, Monounsaturated Fat 0g, Dietary Fiber 4g, Sugars 11g, Total Carbohydrate 20g, Protein 35g.

DAY THREE

BREAKFAST
Crispy Coconut Chicken Fingers
Preparation Time: 15 Minutes
Cooking Time: 15 Minutes
Serving: 4
Ingredients
- 1 tsp garlic powder
- 1/2 cup panko breadcrumbs
- 1/2 cup unsweetened shredded coconut
- 2 eggs, beaten
- 1.33 lbs boneless chicken breast (cut into 16 strips)
- Salt and pepper
- 1 tbsp brown sugar

Preparation
- Preheat the oven to around 400 degrees. Spray with cooking spray on a large baking sheet.
- With salt and pepper, season the chicken. Mix the coconut, panko breadcrumbs, garlic powder, and brown sugar together on a tray. Place

the eggs next to a plate of breadcrumbs in a shallow bowl. Dip in the eggs with each chicken strip and let the excess drip off. Then dredge the coconut breadcrumbs with a strip of chicken. On the prepared baking sheet, put each chicken strip.

- With cooking oil, oil the top of the chicken strips. Bake the chicken strips until light brown, and their internal temperature reaches 165 degrees for 7-8 minutes on each side.

Nutrition

Calories 314, Monounsaturated Fat 0g, Protein 37g, Total Fat 11g, Sodium 106mg, Saturated Fat 7g, Cholesterol 167mg, Total Carbohydrate 12g, Polyunsaturated Fat 0g, Sugars 4g, Dietary Fiber 2g.

LUNCH

Easy Grilled Salmon with Cajun Seasoning

Preparation Time: 15 Minutes

Cooking Time: 15 Minutes

Serving: 4

Ingredients

- 1/2 tsp. garlic powder
- 1 tsp salt
- 1 tsp paprika
- 1/2 tsp. onion powder
- 1.33 lbs. raw wild salmon
- 1 tbsp olive oil
- 1/2 tsp cumin
- 1 tsp black pepper
- 1/2 tsp. oregano
- 1/4 tsp. coriander

Preparation

- Stir paprika, salt, cumin, black pepper, garlic powder, oregano, coriander, and onion powder together.
- Rub the salmon with olive oil and rub in the spice rub. Allow it to rest for 15 minutes.
- Grill it for 8-10 mins over medium-high heat. Depending on your grill and the salmon thickness, adjust this cooking time. This can also be broiled till the fish is cooked through and flaky, for 5-8 minutes.

Nutrition
Calories 257, Saturated Fat 3g, Monounsaturated Fat 3g, Total Fat 13g, Polyunsaturated Fat 3g, Dietary Fiber 1g, Sodium 660mg, Protein 33g, Total Carbohydrate 1g, Cholesterol 68mg, Sugars 0g.

DINNER
Tilapia Fish Burgers
Preparation Time: 10 Minutes
Cooking Time: 10 Minutes
Serving: 4
Ingredients
- 1 tsp. onion powder
- 1/4 cup Panko breadcrumbs
- 1 lb. tilapia
- 1 garlic clove, minced
- 1/2 tsp. basil
- 1 egg white
- 1 egg
- 1 tsp. salt
- 1/2 tsp. black pepper
- 1 tsp. paprika
- 4 reduced-calorie hamburger buns
- 1 tomato, sliced
- 1/2 avocado
- 1 tsp. vegetable oil
- 2 tbsp. Dijon mustard
- 1 cucumber, sliced

Preparation
- Pulse the fish until it's all chopped in a food processor.
- Mix the breadcrumbs, the paprika, the egg, the mustard, the white egg, the salt, the basil, the pepper, the garlic, and the onion powder with the fish.
- Shape into patties. If necessary, place the mixture in the refrigerator for 10 minutes before forming patties. It will help them remain together.
- Brush the burgers with vegetable oil.
- Cook for about 4 mins on each side in a medium-hot skillet.
- Serve with avocado and your favorite burger toppings on toasted buns.

Nutrition
Calories 293, Monounsaturated Fat 0g, Cholesterol 103mg, Total Fat 8g, Sugars 4g, Sodium 1061mg, Total Carbohydrate 28g, Dietary Fiber 6g, Polyunsaturated Fat 0g, Protein 29g, Saturated Fat 2g.

DAY FOUR

BREAKFAST
Healthy Korean Ground Beef with Vegetables
Preparation Time: 5 Minutes
Cooking Time: 15 Minutes
Serving: 4
Ingredients
- 2 tbsp water (more if needed)
- 3 cups mixed Asian vegetables
- 2 garlic cloves, minced
- 2 tbsp. brown sugar (or agave, honey, Stevia to taste)
- 1/4 cup reduced-sodium soy sauce (GF if needed)
- 1 tsp. Asian garlic chili paste (like Sriracha or Sambal Olek)
- 2 tsp sesame oil
- 1 tbsp ginger, minced
- 1.33 lbs. 95% lean ground beef

Preparation
- Heat a pan over high-medium heat. Add the vegetables and water from Asia. Cover and cook until tender and crisp, for 3-4 minutes. Be careful that the vegetables are not overcooked. Add a touch of more water if vegetables tend to stick or burn. Withdraw and set aside.
- To the pan, add the ground beef. Cook until it's cooked through, breaking it up as you go.
- Mix the brown sugar, soy sauce, chili paste, sesame oil, garlic, and ginger together. Add to cooked beef and bring to seethe. For 3-4 minutes, cook.
- Stir in or serve the vegetables on the side, scooping up some of the extra sauce on top.

Nutrition
Calories 293, Monounsaturated Fat 0g, Cholesterol 103mg, Total Fat 8g, Sugars 4g, Sodium 1061mg, Total Carbohydrate 28g, Dietary Fiber 6g, Polyunsaturated Fat 0g, Protein 29g, Saturated Fat 2g

LUNCH
Grilled Pineapple Barbecue Chicken
Preparation Time: 30 Minutes
Cooking Time: 15 Minutes
Serving: 4
Ingredients
- 1/2 cup
- barbecue sauce
- 2 tbsp soy sauce
- 1.33 lbs boneless skinless chicken breast
- 1/4 cup pineapple juice
- 1 garlic clove, minced
- 1 tsp ginger, minced
- 2 cups pineapple, sliced
- 1 tsp Sriracha (optional, more to taste)

Preparation
- Mix the pineapple juice, barbecue sauce, garlic, soy sauce, ginger, and Sriracha together. For at least 30 minutes or overnight, marinate the chicken in this mixture.
- Remove the chicken from the marinade when ready to cook, letting the excess drip off. With cooking oil, oil the pineapple slices. Grill the chicken and pineapple on each side for 4-5 minutes or until they are cooked through. Cook on each side for less time for thinner chicken.
- Meanwhile, into a saucepan, add the leftover marinade. Bring to a boil and cook until slightly reduced, for 4-5 minutes. Serve drizzled with pineapple and chicken.

Nutrition
Calories 270, Saturated Fat 0g, Monounsaturated Fat 0g, Total Fat 2g, Sodium 790mg, Cholesterol 74mg, Protein
33g, Polyunsaturated Fat 0g, Dietary Fiber 2g, Sugars 19g, Total Carbohydrate
25g.

DINNER
Sheet Pan Steak Fajitas
Preparation Time: 15 Minutes
Cooking Time: 15 Minutes
Serving: 4
Ingredients
- 2 limes, juiced
- 3 tbsp fajita seasoning
- 1.33 lbs lean flank steak, sliced thin
- 1 tbsp olive oil
- 2 bell peppers, sliced (any colors)
- 1 red onion, sliced

Preparation
- Start by slicing the flank steak into thin strips using a sharp knife. Based on the size of the flank steak, you can have to cut longer strips by half or thirds. Also, cut the peppers and onions into small pieces.
- Toss the lime juice, olive oil, and fajita seasoning, bell peppers, red onion with the beef, and let it rest for 15-30 minutes. For quick cleanup, I like to do this in a Ziploc bag. When you are short on time, this method can be skipped.
- The oven should be preheated to 425 degrees. Use cooking spray to spray a baking sheet. For easier cleanup, you can also cover it with foil. Layout the vegetables and steak on a single surface on the baking sheet.
- Place in the oven and cook for 10-12 mins, until the vegetables are tender-crisp and the steak is tender. Turn the oven up to broil to put some char and crispiness to the steak for the last 2 minutes of cooking. One important note, when cooked this way, the peppers and onions will still have some bite and texture. If a softer vegetable is preferred, place it in the oven for 10 minutes before adding the steak.

Nutrition
Calories 316, Cholesterol 104mg, Total Fat 13g, Polyunsaturated Fat 1g, Dietary Fiber 3g, Monounsaturated
Fat 4g, Saturated Fat 5g, Sugars 3g, Total Carbohydrate 15g, Sodium 754mg, Protein 34g.

DAY FIVE

BREAKFAST
Air Fryer Crispy Chicken Tenders
Preparation Time: 10 Minutes
Cooking Time: 15 Minutes
Serving: 4

Ingredients
- 1/2 teaspoon seasoned salt
- 1.25 lbs boneless chicken breast tenderloins
- 1/4 cup Panko breadcrumbs
- 2 large eggs, beaten
- 1/2 cup all-purpose flour
- 1/2 cup seasoned breadcrumbs
- 1/2 teaspoon garlic powder
- 1/4 teaspoon black pepper

Preparation
- Preheat the air fryer to 375 ° F. Trim and clean chicken if appropriate
- Set up your breading station. On a plate, place the flour. To a shallow plate or dish, add the beaten eggs. Then add to your plate the seasoned breadcrumbs, garlic powder, Panko breadcrumbs, salt, and pepper. Mix it with a fork. To a shallow plate or dish, add the beaten eggs.
- Begin by dipping one chicken tender into the flour, let the excess fall off. Then dip in the egg, allowing the excess to trickle free. Finish in the breadcrumbs to ensure that the tender is coated uniformly on all sides. With the remaining bids, repeat.
- Spray the air fryer rack with cooking spray. Attach the chicken tenders, leaving a little gap between them. Cook for 8-10 mins or until golden brown and cooked through the offerings. Depending on thickness, accurate cooking time can vary. Cook until all the chicken is cooked. Repeat.

Nutrition

Calories 321, Monounsaturated Fat 0g, Total Carbohydrate 27g, Sugars 1g, Total Fat 4g, Polyunsaturated Fat 0g, Dietary Fiber 1g, Cholesterol 93mg, Saturated Fat 1g, Sodium 398mg, Protein 40g.

LUNCH
Grilled Chicken Sausages and Vegetables

Preparation Time: 5 Minutes
Cooking Time: 15 Minutes
Serving: 4

Ingredients

- 1 summer squash, sliced
- 4 chicken sausages (or turkey)
- 2 zucchinis, sliced
- 1/2 cup basil
- 2 tbsp. olive oil
- 2 tomatoes, sliced
- 3 tbsp. balsamic vinegar
- 1 eggplant, sliced
- Salt and pepper

Preparation

- Lop the vegetable with olive oil, pepper, and salt.
- On the grill, cook the sausages until it is fully cooked or warmed up. This will take 6-8 minutes per side of raw sausages. They need 3-4 minutes per side for pre-cooked sausages.
- On the grill or in a grill basket, cook the vegetables. They should take 3-4 minutes on each side. Chop severely.
- Add the balsamic vinegar to the vegetables and toss with the fresh basil. As required, season with salt and pepper. Serve sausages alongside.

Nutrition

Calories 285, Polyunsaturated Fat 0g, Total Carbohydrate 21g, Saturated Fat 3g, Sodium 503mg, Total Fat 13g, Dietary Fiber 7g, Cholesterol 65mg, Monounsaturated Fat 0g, Sugars 13g, Protein 20g.

DINNER
Portobello Burgers with Swiss Cheese and Avocado
Preparation Time: 30 Minutes
Cooking Time: 15 Minutes
Serving: 4
Ingredients

- 4 slices low-fat Swiss cheese (like Jarlsberg)
- 2 cups arugula
- 1 tbsp olive oil
- 2 tbsp balsamic vinegar
- 1 red onion, sliced
- 1.5 tsp Montreal steak seasoning
- 1 tbsp Worcestershire sauce (vegan if needed)
- 1 tomato, sliced
- 1 tbsp Italian seasoning
- 4 portabella mushroom caps
- 1 avocado, sliced
- 4 reduced-calorie hamburger buns

Preparation

- Stir together the Worcestershire sauce, Italian seasoning, balsamic vinegar, olive oil, and steak seasoning. In this mixture, marinate the mushrooms for a minimum of 30 minutes.
- Remove the mushrooms from the marinade when ready to cook, letting the excess drip off. Grill them on either side for 4-5 minutes. Right before the mushrooms finish cooking, add the cheese, so it melts. Grill the red onions at the same time. Before sticking them on the grill, I usually spray mine with cooking spray or brush it with olive oil.
- Place the tomatoes, arugula, grilled red onion, and avocado on top.

Nutrition
Calories 299, Monounsaturated Fat 1g, Total Fat 13g, Cholesterol 10mg, Dietary Fiber 9g, Saturated Fat 3g, Total
Carbohydrate 36g, Sodium 642mg, Polyunsaturated Fat 0g, Sugars 9g, Protein 15g.

DAY SIX

BREAKFAST
Grilled Hawaiian Chicken Sandwiches
Preparation Time: 30 Minutes
Cooking Time: 15 Minutes
Serving: 4
Ingredients

- ½ tsp Sriracha (optional, more to taste)
- 1/3 cup barbecue sauce
- 1 garlic clove, minced
- 1 jalapeno, sliced
- 1 red onion, sliced
- 1 lb boneless skinless chicken breast
- 3 tbsp pineapple juice
- 1 cup pineapple, sliced
- 4 reduced-calorie hamburger rolls
- 1.5 tbsp soy sauce
- 1 tsp ginger, minced
- 2 cups greens

Preparation

- Stir the garlic, barbecue sauce, soy sauce, pineapple juice, ginger, and Sriracha together. For at least 30 minutes or overnight, marinate the chicken in this mixture.
- Remove the chicken from the marinade when ready to cook, letting the excess drip off. With cooking oil, oil the pineapple slices. Grill the chicken and pineapple on each side for 4-5 minutes or until they are cooked through. For thinner chicken, cook on each side for less time.
- Meanwhile, into a saucepan, add the leftover marinade. Bring to a boil and cook until slightly reduced, for 4-5 minutes. Serve on the sandwiches, drizzled.
- Serve with a layer of sliced red onion, fresh jalapeno, greens, grilled pineapple, greens, and a drizzle of homemade barbecue sauce on the hamburger roll.

Nutrition
Calories 287, Saturated Fat 0g, Polyunsaturated Fat 0g, Total Fat 2g, Cholesterol 56mg, Total Carbohydrate 37g, Sugars 15g, Monounsaturated Fat 0g, Dietary Fiber 4g, Sodium 761mg, Protein29g.

Healthy Greek Yogurt Pancakes

Preparation Time: 5 Minutes

Cooking Time: 10 Minutes

Serving: 4

Ingredients

- 2 eggs
- 1 tbsp baking powder
- 1 tbsp maple syrup
- 1 cup skim or unsweetened nut milk
- 1 tsp vanilla extract
- 1.5 cups white whole wheat flour
- 1/2 cup nonfat plain Greek yogurt (or flavored)

Preparation

- In a mug, whisk the milk, eggs, yogurt, vanilla extract, and maple syrup together.
- Add the baking powder and flour. Stir until they're all mixed. Don't over-mix.
- Over medium heat preheat a nonstick griddle or skillet. Spray with cooking spray. Use 1/4 cup of batter per pancake approximately. Until bubbles shape and begin to pop, cook for 3-4 minutes. Flip over and cook until it is cooked through.

Nutrition

Calories 262, Total Fat 3g, Cholesterol 94mg, Saturated Fat 1g, Polyunsaturated Fat 0g, Dietary Fiber 1g, Monounsaturated Fat 0g, Sodium 348mg, Sugars 8g, Total Carbohydrate 45g, Protein 13g.

DINNER

Sheet Pan Chicken Fajitas

Preparation Time: 30 Minutes

Cooking Time: 15 Minutes

Serving: 4

Ingredients

- 1 tbsp olive oil
- 1 red onion, sliced
- 1.33 lbs boneless chicken breasts, sliced thin
- 2 limes, juiced
- 3 tbsp fajita seasoning
- 2 bell peppers, sliced (any colors)

Preparation

- Lob the olive oil, lime juice, fajita seasoning, and lime juice with the chicken, red onion, and bell peppers and leave to rest for 30 minutes. For quick cleanup, I like to do this in a Ziploc bag. When you are short on time, this move can be skipped.
- To 400 degrees, preheat the oven. Using cooking spray to spray a baking sheet. For more comfortable drying, you can also cover it with foil.
- Spread the chicken and the vegetables on the baking sheet in a single layer. Put in the oven and cook until the chicken is almost cooked through and the vegetables are tender-crisp, for 10-12 minutes. To add some crispiness and char to the chicken for the last 2 minutes of cooking, turn the oven up to broil. One vital note, when cooked this way, the onions and peppers will still have some bite and texture. Put them in the oven for 10 minutes before adding the chicken if you want a softer vegetable.

Nutrition

Calories 257, Monounsaturated Fat 0g, Saturated Fat 1g, Total Carbohydrate 15g, Total Fat 5g, Sugars 3g, Sodium
722mg, Cholesterol 74mg, Dietary Fiber 3g, Polyunsaturated Fat 0g, Protein 33.g

DAY SEVEN

BREAKFAST
Grilled Lemon Chicken with Tzatziki
Preparation Time: 3 Hours
Cooking Time: 15 Minutes
Serving: 4

Ingredients

- 1 clove garlic, minced
- 1/2 lemon, juice, and zest
- 1.33 lbs boneless skinless chicken breast
- 2 tsp dried oregano
- 2 tbsp extra virgin olive oil
- 1/2 tsp dried thyme
- 1 tbsp. dill, chopped
- 3 garlic cloves minced (or garlic powder)
- 1/2 cup plain low-fat yogurt
- Salt and pepper
- 1/2 English cucumber (or Persian cucumbers)

Preparation

- Start by getting the chicken breasts ready. You would want to cut the chicken in half to make two smaller pieces of chicken for more massive chicken breasts. Then pound the chicken to produce breasts that are reasonably uniform in thickness in any dense sections.
- Lemon juice, olive oil, lemon zest, oregano, garlic, salt, thyme, and pepper are all whisked together. A Ziploc bag or jar is attached to the chicken and marinade. Marinate in the refrigerator for at least 2 hours or up to 6 hours. In order to ensure that it is uniformly marinated, rotate the chicken a few times during the marinating process.
- Create tzatziki: Grate the cucumber and suck out all the excess moisture using a paper towel or cheesecloth. Stir it along with the lemon zest, lemon juice, salt, dill, and pepper into the yogurt. For 1 hour or more, refrigerate.
- Preheat the grill when it is ready to cook. Remove the chicken from the marinade and allow the excess to drip away. Cook on each side for 4-6 minutes until it is cooked to 160-165 degrees. Until serving, let it rest for 5 minutes.

Nutrition

Calories 261, Monounsaturated Fat 0g, Total Fat 9g, Sodium 78mg, Saturated Fat 1g, Dietary Fiber 2g, Polyunsaturated Fat 0g, Sugars 3g, Total Carbohydrate 6g, Cholesterol 76mg, Protein 35g.

LUNCH
Roasted Italian Sausages with Potatoes, Peppers, and Onions

Preparation Time: 30 Minutes
Cooking Time: 10 Minutes
Serving: 4

Ingredients

- 1 green pepper
- 1/2 tsp. red pepper flakes
- 4 lean turkey Italian sausages
- 1 onion, chopped
- 1.33 lbs. red potatoes, washed and chopped (Paleo substitute sweet potatoes)
- 1 tbsp. Italian seasoning
- 2 red peppers
- 4 garlic cloves, minced
- 1/4 cup low sodium chicken broth

PREPARATION

- To 400 degrees, preheat the oven.
- To a glass baking dish, add the onion, potatoes, garlic, peppers. Sprinkle the red pepper flakes, salt, olive oil, pepper, and chicken broth with the Italian seasonings. Use your hands and a spoon to toss them together. With a fork, pierce the sausages. Nestle into the vegetables the sausages.
- Bake for 30-35 mins, until the vegetables are cooked and tender. If the vegetables do not brown, position them for 3-4 minutes to brown under the broiler.

Nutrition

Calories 314, Monounsaturated
Fat 0g, Saturated Fat 3g, Total Fat 11g, Cholesterol 60mg, Polyunsaturated Fat 0g, Total Carbohydrate 35g, Dietary Fiber 5g, Sugars 7g, Sodium 707mg, Protein 21.g

DINNER
Baked Carrot Cake Oatmeal with Cream Cheese Glaze
Preparation Time: 10 Minutes

Cooking Time: 45 Minutes

Serving: 6

Ingredients

- 1/4 tsp allspice
- 1/4 tsp. ground ginger
- 2 cups rolled oats
- 1 tsp. cinnamon
- 1/2 cup natural applesauce or pineapple
- 1/4 cup reduced-fat cream cheese
- 2 tbsp unsweetened shredded coconut
- 1/4 cup raisins
- 1/4 cup maple syrup (add according to taste preference)
- 1 cup chopped fresh carrots
- 1/2 tsp. vanilla extract
- 1 Pinch salt
- 2 cups unsweetened almond milk
- 2 eggs
- 1 tbsp chia seeds (optional)
- 1 tbsp powdered sugar (or maple syrup)
- 1/8 tsp. nutmeg (optional)
- 1 tbsp warm water

Preparation

- Preheat the oven to 400 ° C. Use cooking spray to spray 8 x 8 baking dishes. In a cup, blend together the oats, applesauce, carrots, coconut, raisins, spices, chia seeds, and salt. For a more traditional carrot cake, you can add walnuts or pecans as well.
- Whisk the almond milk, maple syrup, eggs, and vanilla extract together in another dish. Attach the mixture of oatmeal and whisk it together.
- Pour it into the dish for baking. Bake until the oatmeal is fully set and lightly browned, for 40-50 minutes.
- Meanwhile, the powdered sugar, milk, cream cheese, and vanilla are beaten together to make the glaze. To make it easier to stir, you should microwave the cream cheese for a few seconds.
- Remove the baked oatmeal from the oven and leave to cool for 15 minutes or more. Drizzle the top with the glaze and serve. Keep the leftovers for 4-5 days in the fridge

Chapter 3: Anti-Inflammatory Diet Plan

Some of our bodies are lit on the inside, and some of our habits are the same as throwing fuel into this flame.

How to put the fire out or at least regulate it again?

To summarize, inflammation is the chemical reaction of the body to try to defend itself. It aims at eliminating harmful stimuli such as bacteria, damaged cells, and irritants; this is the first step in the process of healing.

Inflammation activates an immune system response. Initially, inflammation is helpful since it is used for protection, but inflammation can also lead to more (Chronic) inflammation that causes serious health problems.

The five symptoms of inflammation are pain, heat, redness, swelling and function loss!

First of all, what causes inflammation?

- Chronic inflammation
- Obsession
- Eco-toxins (water, food and air)
- Stress physiological
- Intensive exercise / stamina
- Trauma emotional
- Era
- Autoimmune condition
- If you find the food is in the brackets for toxins.
- Every food we eat receives a body reaction.

There are some foods in many people's diets today that cause inflammation to increase. You could possibly imagine what kind of foods are (fried foods, fake foods, refined foods, good coffee, alcohol, carbohydrates).

The anti-inflammatory diet involves a lot of foods that I have suggested to help avoid and minimize inflammation for other purposes.

It's a very familiar way to improve your health and recover from disease or injury.

Without inflammation, you can become much healthier and less likely to develop any particularly dangerous diseases in the long term.

And what is the anti-inflammatory diet?

The diet consists of a number of naturally nutritious foods. No processed foods are available, and everything is organic and safe.

Here are the primary foods in the anti-inflammatory diet:

Battle fats with inflammation!

A significant proportion of the anti-inflammatory diet is good fats. Foods rich in Omega-3 fatty acids have proved to be anti-inflammatory, and I, therefore, recommend eating as many of these to help reduce inflammation.

Fish is an excellent source, so it is preserved in sardines, tuna, herring and anchovies. Extra virgin coconut oil, olive oil, Avocado oil and walnuts are other good sources.

Rich vegetables and fruit antioxidant

Vegetables and Fruits are filled with antioxidants and vitamins, some of which are anti-inflammatory. Onions, lettuce, sweet potato, garlic, broccoli, and other green leafy vegetables are some of the best vegetable sources.

Blueberries, papaya, strawberries and bananas are healthy fruits and berries to look for. They are filled with high antioxidant levels that are ideal for such a diet.

The protein of good quality

What proteins are really essential to consume? There is a vast difference between cheap meats and organic meats fed with grass. Cheap meat is most likely filled with hormones and pesticides contributing to inflammation, while organic grass-fed meat helps to combat inflammation.

Choose your meat carefully and go as much as you can for the omega-3 packaged grass-fed variants. Using this law when eggs are also involved. Steak, eggs, fish, and beans (legumes). Steak.

These three food forms are the foundation of the anti-inflammatory diet.

Ingredients that minimize inflammation and help to restrict dangerous free racial development are also found in herbs, including ginger, curcumin, turmeric, oregano and rosemary.

Food to avoid an anti-inflammation diet at all costs

I just mentioned the foods that can reduce inflammation and keep you healthy. These foods that I'm about to list are the foods that cause inflammation, and you really should avoid them. It's an act of equilibrium.

Pro Inflammatory Foods:

- Processed Food
- Fast food and take aways-particularly deep-fried foods
- Omega 6 fats-in many oils such as sunflower and soy oil can be found.
- Bread-most products containing wheat and gluten
- Every trans-fat
- Sugar and meal
- Bacon and willows
- Margarine

Start your anti-inflammatory diet tips.

The first steps, as with many healthy diets, are to start taking out the foods you carry.

So, if you eat any of the above foods daily, you need to start taking them out. Eating such food in an anti-inflammatory diet totally undermines the intent of what you want to do and will ruin your results.

Even if you don't experience inflammation but want to change your eating habits, you can still follow this kind of diet. It will significantly improve your fitness and aid you with weight loss.

The next step is to start incorporating anti-inflammatory foods into your diet. Start by adding safe omega-3 fats. Start using your vegetables with extra virgin olive oil, cocoa oil with cooking, start snacking with nuts rather than crisps and eat fresher fish as well as high-quality fish oil substitute.

I hope you consume a lot of fruits and vegetables already in your diet, if not, you can start adding them now.

Variety is the best things about fruit and veg.

Hundreds of different types of fruit and vegetables are available, all filled with goodness and FLAVOUR.

Drink green tea – Drinking green tea has demonstrably been anti-inflammatory. Flavonoids in tea have anti-inflammatory compounds that indicate that the risk of many infections and diseases have been decreased.

Experiment with herbs and spices - add life and mix things together. Many people add salt, sugar, mayonnaise and other simple choices while cooking. Start adding garlic, cayenne, turmeric, ginger, and other herbs and spice to the meal instead.

Take out foods that cause issues - If you notice that you are intolerant or that you have trouble with those foods after feeding, take them off entirely. Many people get bad reactions from food containing wheat and gluten, so try to cut out these foods to see if there is a difference. Eliminate the food you think will cause problems one by one, and soon the guilty party will be uncovered!

Inflammation - Eating Anti-Inflammatory Foods

Are there diets that can minimize inflammation? Do they work? Do they work? Scientists have found that part of what we eat and inflammation have a connection. Some compounds in food have been identified that can minimize inflammation and others that can stimulate it. Many details still remain to be learned about the way diet and inflammation interact, and research is not currently done to decide which particular foods or food classes are beneficial to people with arthritis. We start to see more clearly how to eat the best way to decrease inflammation.

So why do we care so much about inflammation? The body's natural protection against diseases and injuries is inflammation. The body's immune system acts to inflame the region that serves to get rid of the invader or cure the wound if anything goes wrong. Inflammation can cause swelling, discomfort, heat and redness, but it disappears until the issue is resolved. This is a healthy swelling.

We can have chronic inflammation, a form that people with RA, lupus, psoriasis and other "inflammatory" arthritis are familiar with. Chronic inflammation is the kind that won't be gone. All the forms of arthritis listed above are an immune system disorder that causes inflammation and does not know when to shut down. Inflammatory arthritis, chronic inflammation, lifelong disability and tissue damage may have significant effects if it is not treated correctly. An entire host of other medical problems is associated with inflammation.

Inflammation has been shown to lead to atherosclerosis, which raises the risk of heart disease as fat builds up on the lining of the arteries. There have also been elevated levels of inflammatory proteins in the blood of cardiovascular patients. Inflammation was also linked with obesity, asthma, diabetes, and even Alzheimer's disease and cancer. Scientists agree that even though the level is minimal, a persistent level of inflammation in the body may have several adverse effects. Research shows that diet could reduce inflammation; theoretically, a lower inflammation diet may affect a variety of health conditions.

Researchers searched for answers in our early ancestors' dietary patterns to see what foods could better help us. You think these practices are more in line with the way the body absorbs and uses what we eat and drink. The diet of our ancestors was wild meats (venison or boar) and wild vegetables (green, leafy, fruit and berries). Before the agricultural revolution (around 10,000 years ago) there were no cereal grains. There was very little milk and no processed or refined food. Our diets typically consist of high amounts of meat, saturated (or insufficient) fats and refined foods, and exercise is low. Nearly anything we eat is available near or far from our computer with a mouse click.

Our lifestyles and diet are way out of the way our bodies are made from inside. While our genetic makeup has very little changed since our early days, our diet and behaviors have drastically changed, and the changes have worsened in the last 50-100 years. Our genes didn't have the ability to adapt. We don't give the bodies a right fuel, and it is as if we think of our bodies as jet engines when they are like the engine of the very early aircraft. Some foods we put into our bodies, in particular, because we eat so many of them have a terrible impact on our health.

There are two nutrients in our foods, which have been drawn to our foods for thousands of years, omega-3 fatty acids and omega-6 fatty acids. It is a component in almost all of our many cells and is essential for normal development and growth. These two acids play an inflammatory role. In many studies, it was found that some omega-3 sources in particular lead to the reduction of the inflammation and that omega-6 enhances it.

Today, the problem is that the average American is about fifteen times higher than omega-six on average. Whilst our very early ancestors consumed Omega 3 and Omega 6 in equal proportion, this is thought to have helped to regulate their ability to start and off inflammation. We assume that the imbalance of omega-3 and omega-6 in our diets leads to the abundance of swelling in our bodies.

So why are we now eating so many omega-6s? Omega 6 is found in vegetable oils, such as safflower oil, maize oil, cottonseed oil, sunflower oil, soy oil and their products, for example, margarine. Also, many of the packaged snack foods available today are packed with these oils. Instead of fatty foods, including butter and lard, vegetable oils were used on the basis of the best knowledge of the time. The effects of this advice could contribute to the increased consumption of omega-6, causing omega-6 and omega-3 imbalances.

Omega 6s can be present in other popular foods including meats and egg yolks. Omega 6 in meat is the fatty acids found in grain-fed animals like cows, lambs, pigs and chickens. Most meat in the US is fed grain, unlike their cousins which contain less fatty acids. Wild game like venison and squid are lower in Omega 6's and fat in omega 3's and higher than the meat we shop in the supermarkets.

In both animal and plant food, you will get omega-3s. Our bodies can more readily transform omega-three from animal sources into anti-inflammatory compounds than omega-three from plant sources. Plant food contains hundreds of other safe compounds, many of which are anti-inflammatory and thus do not minimize them all together.

Many foods are high in omega 3s, including fatty fish, especially fish from cold waters. Of course, everybody knows about salmon, but you knew that in mackerel, anchovies, herring, striped bass and bluefish omega 3s could be found. Wild fish are also generally considered to be better sources of omega-3 than farm fish. Eggs enriched with omega-3 oils can also be bought. In herbs, leafy greens (such as kale, spinach and chard), as well as flaxseed, wheat germ, walnuts and their oils, there are many excellent sources of omega 3s.

You may also have omega-3s (often like fish oil) in supplements; this source has in some cases been shown to be helpful. Before you take a fish oil supplement, you should take it with your doctor because it may interfere with certain drugs and can raise the risk of bleeding in some circumstances. An individual is taking a prescription omega-three supplement because his doctor told him the additives that you get from supermarket and health food store are not pure. Other fats, known as pro-inflammatory, lead to obstructed arteries, the "poor" or saturated fats contained by meats and high-fat dairy foods.

Trans-fats are still relatively new to the cause of cardiovascular disease. These trans-fats can be present in packaged foods and snacks and can be shown by reading the labels. They can be classified as partially hydrogenated oils, often soy oils or cotton oils. However, they can naturally also occur in small quantities in animal food. The theory is that they contribute to the pro-inflammatory behavior in our bodies, and the quantities we consume now are exceptional.

Antioxidants are compounds which prevent "free radicals" from taking over our bodies from inflammation. Plant foods, e.g. vegetables, berries, seeds and nuts, contain massive levels of antioxidants (including beans). Olive oil and walnut oil are also very strong antioxidant sources. These foods have long been considered the fundamentals of health and can be found with vivid and vibrant pigments in fruits and vegetables. The more colorful the plant, the better it's for you, from green, particularly leafy, to low-starch vegetables such as broccoli and cauliflower, to fruit berries and tomatoes, to bright orange and yellow, fruit and vegetables.

I bet you are curious about what Arthritis is all about. Well, some studies has been carried out on diet and arthritis, primarily on RA. The research analyzed a lot of other diet and RA studies and found that diets rich in omega 3 have an effect on minimizing RA symptoms. Another research found that consuming omega-six fatty acids and omega-three fatty acids in a ratio of 2 to 3 (a poor ratio in most people's diets from 15 to 1) have reduced inflammation in people with RA. Another research was found that taking omega-3 often helps people to decrease their use of naproxen and ibuprofen (Advil, Motrin) without steroidal anti-inflammatory drugs (NSAIDs). But such and other research is not sufficient evidence to demonstrate that a specific anti-inflammatory diet may have a real effect on the symptoms of arthritis. This does not mean that diets are harmful; it only means that science will prove its advantages one day. In the future, diet, exercise and medicine will be considered one of the several methods to relieve the effects of arthritis.

We don't have to return fully to the guy in the cave to take the anti-inflammatory diet. Only eating a balanced diet, which is today recommended, is on track. Our primary strategy should be to match the number of contemporary foods with foods that were long ago rich in food inflammation. All we have to do is replace omega-six rich food with omega-3 rich foods, cut off how much of our meat and poultry we consume a few days a week while eating oily fish and add more vibrant fruit and vegetables, and even though whole grains were not a part of our early antiquity diet, it should be included in ours. Make sure the whole grain is not processed, since it contains several beneficial nutrients and inflammatory compounds. Researchers have found that consuming many high-sugar and white flour foods can promote inflammation.

The amount of knowledge we have about how the body functions and how our ancestor eats helps to validate this old saying: "You are what you eat." But we have to learn even more before we can recommend any anti-inflammatory diet. Our genetic make-up and the seriousness of our wellbeing will decide the advantages of an anti-inflammatory diet, and regrettably, we have doubts as to that diet.

What we eat or don't eat, too, is a small part of the whole story. We are not as involved physically as our forefathers, and physical exercise has its own anti-inflammatory effects. Our ancestors were also much slimmer than ourselves, and body fat is an active tissue which can produce inflammatory compounds.

Anti-inflammatory food is a way to choose foods that are more in line with the needs of the body. By returning to our origins, we will achieve a more healthy diet. Looking at the diet of the people of the Bible, you will find that, like our ancestors, they were much more active and their diets were much the same as our ancestors of the caves. They also had no choice but to go anywhere, no cars or vans. They chose to go. Although today is better, our health has suffered a lot.

Ten Anti Inflammatory Foods to Add to Your Diet for Pain Relief

Although more Americans are looking for traditional homeopathic and natural medicine for arthritis, gout and various other muscle, joint and sore pains, the easiest and cheapest home remedies will add some top foods to the American diet. A shortlist of anti-inflammatory health foods is available here.

1 - Fish are loaded with anti-inflammatory omega-3 fatty acids, especially cold-water fish, like salmon, tropics or tuna. Many studies confirm that adding fish (or fish oil) to a diet will decrease inflammation.

Choose your fish carefully. There's a great deal of discussion between wild and farm fish. Wild fish tend to be higher in nutrients and lower in fat than farms due to their diet and exercise. On average, agricultural fish have about 20% less protein and 20% more fat than wild fish. Tiny fish, shrimp and red krill consume wild fish, which is the root of the surplus of omega-3 EFAs. They are also free to exercise and reduce their fat content.

Farm-grown fish are fed pellets of fishmeal, generally, ground, mackerel, sardines, anchovies, and some smaller fish, which do not contain omega three high concentrations as wild food sources. To emulate the deep red colors of wild fish, in particular salmon, most farmed fish are fed a color with their meal. Since fish farms are small, overcrowded net enclosures or stallions, fish are fed antibiotics to manage infections, diseases and parasites.

High mercury levels, both in the wild and in farmed fish, have also been reported: wild fish from polluted waters and farmed fish from mercury pollution in their feed. Mercury in fish, primarily builds up in the skin, so do not eat any fish from the skin.

2 – Virgin extra virgin is an excellent oleic acid source, inflammatory oil. It also stimulates the role of insulin, thereby reducing blood sugar. Olive oil is not suitable for deep-frying due to its small smoke point, but it is ideal for healthy cooking choices such as sauté and braising. Cook with olive oil or shortens rich in unhealthy trans-fats instead of oils.

3-Oleic acid nuts, cashews, walnuts, and a variety of other nuts, as well as fiber, omega-3 fatty acids, protein, and other good phytochemicals. Since some nuts are really fat, make sure they eat moderately.

4-Grapes; Researchers say that grapes with a high concentration of flavonoids have anti-inflammatory properties, they claim. According to today's medical journal, "Now researchers at the Johns Hopkins University School of Medicine have shown that powdered grapes tend to decrease pain and inflammation in a rat model of arthritis, where the knee of rats is inflamed with chemical injection."

5-Cherries are a rich source of antioxidants, especially tardive cherries. They contain large quantities of anthocyanin's, one of the most potent antioxidants, which give a rich red color to the cherries. A study of scientists and colleagues from the Agricultural Research Service (ARS) indicates that cherries can both reduce painful arthritis and reduce the risk of other inflammatory conditions, such as cardiovascular disease and cancer.

6-Green Tea contains flavonoids, known as "catechins" which are an unfermented tea. Catechins are potent antioxidants that are killed by other teas during the processing and fermentation process. Green tea contains about 27% catechins as compared to oolong (partly fermented) with 23% and black tea (fermented) with approximately 4%. Animal tests have shown that green tea decreased the incidence of arthritis substantially. Green tea affects arthritis. It causes changes in the immune system of arthritis.

You may have an allergy, as many people discover if you discover that you have headaches after you eat teas. Listen to your body and watch what works, as always.

7-Leafy Greens Green leafy vegetables are packed with fiber, antioxidants and omega-3s, such as spinach and kale. Look for organic products or wash thoroughly in order to remove pesticides and chemicals which tend to accumulate on a leaves.

8 Broccoli, the compound of 3.3 'diindolylmethane (DIM) found in broccoli, cauliflower and its kissing cousins has been shown to combat inflammatory effects and to improve the immune system. These super-veggies often contain Sulphur, a phytonutrient that helps the liver work and enhances the natural detoxification potential of your body. Eat raw or burn to retain beneficial nutrients (frozen varying vegetables lose a great deal of nutritional value) that can be broken down by food preparation such as boiling or frying.

9 – Apples and red onions contain quercetin, a chemical that, along with other antioxidants, has proved to have anti-inflammatory properties. The bulk of quercetin is in their skin. So don't peel apples until you eat them. This is what gives them a rich red hue. Rinse all new fruits and vegetables long before you feed to kill pesticides and fertilizers.

\# 10 – Water; The fresher you drink, the cleaner you drink, the better. More than 70 % water made up of your body, and a constant filling helps to keep contaminants, including muscles, joints, and blood, flushed out of your system.

The growing popularity of bottled water has led to a heated debate about tap water versus bottled water in recent years. You should know what the discrepancies are and determine what is best for you.

A variety of options are available on the market today in bottled water, from spring water, mineral water and sparkling water. While some come from natural sources and other uncontaminated sources, more than 25% of the water sold originates in municipal sources.

The Easiest Changes to Boost Health

There are million and one trendy diets that change your look and feel in a few days. The customer is inundated with products that make their skin "appear" healthier and smoother. In a world that focuses so much on looking good and being safe, there's one diet that can make the body safe and live longer.

Today the anti-inflammatory diet has so many applications that it is shocking that anyone has never made the most comfortable lifestyle changes, nor has health and beauty gurus made on the new trend in weight loss, appearance and anti-aging. The truth is that the anti-inflammatory diet will do what most diets suggest they are capable of doing and improve their lifespan.

So how do I begin the anti-inflammatory diet?

Get a paper and write in a given week all the foods you consume. Think of the first week as the natural time to eat, so don't make any adjustments or eat something you usually don't eat. When the list is over, go to the Internet and read a little bit about the power of food against inflammation. Many people are shocked by the obviously nutritious foods that can affect overall body health and disease prevention. Of course, the industry screams to customers that they drink more vitamin C and that they minimize calories, but what about foods that look good but are really not? These foods are available after a week of journaling before your anti-inflammatory diet starts.

Are baked foods on the list? Opportunities are if these foods have been pre-packaged; they contain at least a small amount of trans-fat. Even the tiny 100 calorie cupcake bites, sold as suitable alternatives, can hold up to 0.5 grams of trans-fats. Eating only two of these small cakes a day for a week adds a large amount of 7 g trans-fats – the only safe level is 0 g.

Have you been eating a salad this week? Many people assume that eating a salad is a healthier option even without this fat, laden, green dressing. One daily dressing tablespoon can contain 100 calories and approximately 10 grams of fat. The average true serving is about 1/4 cup per salad. This corresponds to 400 calories, 40 grams of fat and the inflammation factor scale of -76, which measures the overall inflammatory impact of food on the body. The aim is to hit +50 or higher.

Few people look at the food in an offensive manner. However, the fact is that many widespread life-threatening illnesses are associated with inflammation. Choosing foods without trans fats and low total fats is a safe option to develop your anti-inflammatory response. These modifications are comfortable, and everybody can still jump to the diet.

Foods Hurting the Anti-Inflammatory Diet

You have opted to eat an anti-inflammatory diet, take back your life and health. Many people want to tackle obesity, arthritis, diabetes and other inflammatory disorders in the same way. As with any dietary changes, the control over the foods consumed will grow lax after a while. The same diet also falls back into the diet and limits the potency of the anti-inflammatory diet. These include frozen food, oil mixtures and margarine. The other prevalent factors are the reduction of protein and water consumption.

Packaged food is clearly bad for the body. These foods also contain too much sodium. While it can seem innocuous to eat a meal two or three times a week by microwave, the effect can be dramatic. Prepackaged foods have an average of between 700 and 1000 calories each. Just three meals a week will add another 3,000 calories to your diet, not to mention fat and sodium rises. High-fat foods induce hours of inflammation in the body which can contribute to weight growth that increases inflammation.

On a budget, oil mixtures are better than pure olive oil. However, these mixtures can include oils containing trans-fats. Fats are unhealthy and must not be eaten in any diets.

Margarine is less expensive and has fewer calories than butter. Some people also feel that consuming pure butter will lead to an increase in cholesterol that can lead to stroke. That's NOT the case. People who decide to consume deficient carbohydrate diets, often with large intakes of butter, calculate lower levels of cholesterol than margarine or low-fat eaters.

Protein is costly, and the budget will split the lean protein. If money is tight, this may seem like a harmless option to buy the fatty burger to replace 93/7 lean beef in your anti-inflammatory diet. Red fatty meat is associated with increased cancer risk and induces inflammation in the body. Instead, try to replace the burger, all beans together.

Water is a fluid of life, and drinking water is the best option to improve wellbeing and decrease inflammation overall. Some began an anti-inflammatory diet of a half-gallon or more of water a day. Over time, negligent behavior may contribute to increased intakes of caffeine and a decreased intake of water. Caffeine is associated with inflammation and can reduce inflammation in the anti-inflammatory diet.

The anti-inflammatory diet does not ban all foods that can increase inflammation. The first reason people scrap new diets and stick to old eating habits is deprivation. Instead of depriving them, consider healthy alternatives or simply eliminate pre-packaged foods by consuming red fatty and trans-fatty oils. It's not the problem once in a while. It is when inflammation returns every week or every day once in a while, even though you feel you are on an anti-inflammatory diet.

Conclusion

Natural anti-inflammatory medications are prescribed, and people are well informed now on what is right and wrong for them. Clearly, going to the burger bar every day, or eating large amounts of food is terrible for you and should be avoided. A diet based on natural anti-inflammatory agents is one of the best ways of alleviating inflammatory pain.

Natural remedies are what we should look at. Besides what we should eat, we should avoid a whole host of foods. Our consumption of red meat, milk products, and saturated fats should be limited. Instead of palm oil, we can cook foods with olive oil and cut them on animal proteins.

A diet based on natural anti-inflammatory drugs is now commonly used and is intended to help preserve your health and also affect chronic inflammation problems (people with heart disease, many cancers, and other diseases).

CPSIA information can be obtained
at www.ICGtesting.com
Printed in the USA
BVHW040719080321
601987BV00031B/1036